Understanding the Universe: An Introduction to Astronomy

Part I:
Unlocking the Secrets of the Heavens

Professor Alex Filippenko

THE TEACHING COMPANY ®

PUBLISHED BY:

THE TEACHING COMPANY
4151 Lafayette Center Drive, Suite 100
Chantilly, Virginia 20151-1232
1-800-TEACH-12
Fax—703-378-3819
www.teach12.com

ISBN 1-56585-643-0

Alex Filippenko, Ph.D.

Professor of Astronomy at the
University of California at Berkeley

Alex Filippenko is a Professor of Astronomy at the University of California at Berkeley. After receiving his B.A. in Physics from the University of California at Santa Barbara (1979) and his Ph.D. in Astronomy from the California Institute of Technology (1984), he moved to UC Berkeley as a Miller Fellow for Basic Research in Science. He was appointed to the UC Berkeley faculty in 1986 and received tenure in 1988, and he has been a senior member of the Center for Particle Astrophysics since 1989. His main research interests are supernovae (exploding stars), active galaxies, black holes, and observational cosmology, and he has also spearheaded efforts to develop completely robotic telescopes. The results of his work have been reported in more than 260 scientific publications, and in about 280 abstracts and astronomical circulars. He has also edited two technical books. His research accomplishments have been recognized with several major awards, including the Newton Lacy Pierce Prize of the American Astronomical Society and the Robert M. Petrie Prize of the Canadian Astronomical Society. He has served as Councilor of the American Astronomical Society, and is currently on the Board of Directors of the Astronomical Society of the Pacific.

A dedicated and enthusiastic instructor, Professor Filippenko has won the top two teaching awards at UC Berkeley, and in 1995 he was voted "Best Professor" on campus in an informal student poll. He has delivered more than 130 public lectures on astronomy. Television, radio, newspaper, and magazine reporters frequently contact him for interviews about his work and that of others, and he has also participated in televised NASA Space Science Updates. During the past few years he has played a prominent role in educational videos and television documentaries, most notably the widely viewed "Mysteries of Deep Space" and "Stephen Hawking's Universe." He will co-author a revised edition of Professor Jay M. Pasachoff's popular textbook, "Journey Through the Universe" (2000), called *The Cosmos: Astronomy in the New Millenium* in its new edition.

Table of Contents

Understanding the Universe:
An Introduction to Astronomy
Part I: Unlocking the Secrets of the Heavens

Professor Biography i
Course Scope 1
Lecture One   A Grand Tour of the Cosmos 4
Lecture Two   Journey Through Space and Time 26
Lecture Three   Light—The Supreme Informant 46
Lecture Four   The Fingerprints of Atoms 67
Lecture Five   Tools of the Trade 92
Lecture Six   Space Telescopes and the Celestial Sphere.... 117
Lecture Seven   Our Sun—The Nearest Star 142
Lecture Eight   Lunar Phases and Glorious Eclipses 165
Glossary 192
Timelines 202
Biographical Notes 205
Credits 209

Understanding the Universe:
An Introduction to Astronomy

Scope:

This visually rich course is designed to provide a non-technical description of modern astronomy, including the structure and evolution of planets, stars, galaxies, and the Universe as a whole. Astronomical objects are explored with breathtaking data obtained by the Hubble Space Telescope, planetary probes, and other modern instruments. We consider amazing things like quasars, exploding stars, neutron stars, and black holes, and we show how they increase our understanding of the physical principles of nature. Recent newsworthy topics such as the tentative evidence of primitive life on Mars, the detection of planets around other stars, and the possible discovery of a long-range repulsive force are investigated. Scientifically reasonable speculations regarding the birth of the Universe and the probability of extraterrestrial life are included.

We concentrate on the most exciting aspects of our fantastic Universe, and on the methods by which astronomers have developed an understanding of it. The lectures present, in clear and simple terms, explanations of how the Universe "works," as well as the interrelationships between its different components. Reliance on basic mathematics and physics is minimal, but appropriate in some sections to deepen the interested viewer's quantitative understanding of the material.

The course is divided into five major parts, each consisting of eight lectures. In the first part we provide an introduction to the Universe and to some of the techniques used to study it. Various commonly observed phenomena such as rotation of the celestial sphere, seasons, lunar phases, and eclipses are also discussed. Part II focuses on studies of our Solar System, from ancient times to the present. We summarize the major properties of planets and their moons, and obtain a better appreciation of the factors that affect them. Stars and their lives are the subject of Part III. We discuss the method by which stars generate energy, explain the creation of the heavy elements necessary for life, and explore the bizarre fates of different types of stars. In Part IV we extend our studies to the giant collections of stars called galaxies, along the way examining evidence for massive black holes and other dark matter. The search for other planets and alien life is also described. The final part deals with the birth, structure, and fate of the entire Universe. We consider the evidence that the Universe began at a finite time in the past, and outline the consequences of its early evolution. The expansion and geometry of the Universe are discussed.

Learning Objectives:

Upon completion of Part I of this lecture series, you should be able to:

1. Describe a few of the exciting topics being investigated by modern astronomers.

2. Outline some of the key events in the history of the Universe that led to the presence of humans.

3. Explain how the finite speed of light allows astronomers to look back in time, providing a "fossil record" of the Universe.

4. Construct a scale model of the Universe that illustrates the relative distances and sizes of various objects.

5. Discuss the nature of electromagnetic radiation, and state its speed in terms of wavelength and frequency.

6. Define what is meant by a spectrum, and identify the region of the electromagnetic spectrum that visible light occupies.

7. Distinguish between the wave and particle aspects of light.

8. Describe the basic properties of an atom, including its constituent particles and electronic structure.

9. Discuss the formation of absorption and emission lines in a spectrum, in terms of the interaction of photons with atoms.

10. Explain how astronomers can determine the chemical composition of a distant object.

11. Describe the Doppler effect, and use it to calculate the velocity of an object along your line of sight.

12. Discuss the main purposes of telescopes, and sketch the paths that light rays follow in different types of telescopes.

13. Describe the factors that influence the clarity of an image obtained with a telescope.

14. Explain why some telescopes, such as the Hubble Space Telescope, are placed above the Earth's atmosphere.

15. Summarize the way in which the night sky changes over the course of a night and a year, as well as from different locations on Earth.

16. State the physical reason for the changing seasons on Earth.

17. Discuss what physicists mean by a "black body" and how this concept relates to the light emitted by the Sun and stars.

18. Summarize the various outer parts of the Sun, describe the solar activity cycle, and explain why sunspots are dark.

19. Illustrate how the phases of the Moon, lunar eclipses, and solar eclipses are produced.

20. Describe how measurements during a total solar eclipse helped confirm Einstein's general theory of relativity.

Lecture One
A Grand Tour of the Cosmos

Scope:

This is the first lecture of Part I, *Unlocking the Secrets of the Heavens*. We are in a golden age of astronomy. Amazing discoveries are being made at a rapid pace with powerful new instruments such as the Hubble Space Telescope. This visually rich course is designed to share with you the excitement and magnificence of the Universe. The second major goal is to demonstrate that astronomy is an investigation of our origins, and of our place in the cosmos. It is also important to show how the process of science is actually conducted. The lectures focus on concepts and qualitative explanations, but brief technical descriptions are given for those who wish to see more of the mathematical and physical details. This first lecture provides an overview of astronomy, with photographs of many representative objects and quick summaries of some major ideas.

Objectives

Upon completion of this lecture, you should be able to:

1. Describe briefly some of the exciting topics being investigated by astronomers.
2. State the primary goals of this course.
3. List some of the main constituents of the Universe.
4. Explain, generally, what scientists are trying to accomplish with their studies.

Outline

I. This is one of the most exciting times in the history of astronomy.

    A. Discoveries are being made at a rapid pace with powerful new instruments such as the Hubble Space Telescope and the Keck telescopes.

    B. Hardly a week goes by without an astronomical news story, and major headlines appear almost monthly. Some examples from the last decade of the millennium include the following.

1. Planets have been detected orbiting other stars.
2. Tentative evidence for primitive (microbial) life on Mars has been found.
3. The process by which stars are created from clouds of gas and dust has been examined.
4. The existence of black holes has been convincingly shown.
5. The birth and evolution of galaxies has been studied.
6. Tiny ripples in the distribution of material have been detected early in the history of the Universe, and it is from these fluctuations, that clusters of galaxies formed.
7. We have witnessed collisions between galaxies that induce giant bursts of star formation.
8. Colossal explosions have been seen billions of light years away.
9. The age of the Universe has been measured fairly accurately.
10. There is intriguing evidence that the Universe may be accelerating its expansion rate.

C. One of my main goals is to simply share with you the excitement and magnificence of the Universe.

1. If you are brand new to astronomy, just curious about what you've seen and heard, I want to teach enough of the basics to allow you to more fully comprehend and enjoy popular articles and television programs. I want to introduce you to some of the most mind-boggling concepts imaginable.

2. If you already know some astronomy and like it, I want to heighten your fascination with the subject, and to show you the richness and beauty of many interrelated topics.

3. For the real astronomy enthusiasts among you, I'd like to reinforce and extend your knowledge, provide some subtle insights, and expose you to a few ideas that you may have never considered.

4. In any case, I'd like all of you to leave with a lifelong interest in astronomy.

II. A second major goal is to show you that astronomy is a quest for our origins, our place in the cosmos.

A. How did we get here, and where are we going? For example:

1. What is the Milky Way Galaxy?
2. How did the Earth form?
3. From where came the elements of which we are made?
4. What is the fate of the Sun?
5. Are there other intelligent creatures out there?

B. Most of us have gazed with wonder at the stars and asked some of these questions. This is part of what makes astronomy such a personal and popular science.

C. Since this is a survey course, I won't be able to go into many details, but I'll give you the foundation you'll need for further explorations.
  1. Socrates said, "Education is the kindling of a flame, not the filling of a vessel."
  2. It is in this spirit that I teach the course. I hope you will continue to learn more about our origins and place in the cosmos.

III. Another of my goals is to give you some idea of *how* science is done, and also to convey the thrill of scientific discovery.

A. Science is a dynamic process: new ideas are developed and tested, and modified when necessary. Scientists want to figure out how things work.
  1. In physics, we try to determine the fundamental laws, and use them to understand the many complex aspects of nature. Astronomy is the exploration of celestial phenomena, and the application of physics to such studies.
  2. Ideally, a scientific hypothesis should not only explain what is already known, but make a prediction of a previously unobserved phenomenon. If subsequent experiments confirm the prediction, belief in the hypothesis is strengthened.

B. Some of our views at the cutting edge of astronomy are changing yearly. What is said here reflects the state of knowledge in mid-1998, and part of it may be out of date shortly.

C. But there are certain foundations that are unlikely to change, and upon which we can build.

1. The concept of atoms, for example, has been proven beyond any reasonable doubt.
2. Similarly, Newton's laws of motion are extremely accurate within their realm of applicability.

D. I will try to indicate which parts of the course are the most speculative and uncertain.

E. I will *not* use science to conclude why humans are here, or the reason for the existence of the laws of physics. These questions are more in the realm of theology, philosophy, and metaphysics.

IV. This will be a visually rich course, with many photographs from the Hubble Space Telescope, planetary probes, and other modern instruments.

A. Although the photographs are not reproduced in these notes, many of them can be found in standard textbooks on astronomy.

B. The books I especially recommend as companions to the videos are listed at the end of this first lecture's outline. Many of the diagrams shown in the videos can also be found in these books.

C. The course is mostly descriptive, non-technical, and non-mathematical. I will focus on concepts and qualitative explanations.
1. Nevertheless, astronomy is a *physical* science, and many viewers do want a quantitative component.
2. Hence, where appropriate, I will introduce simple mathematical and physical relationships.
3. The quantitative aspects will serve as an introduction; I will generally not go into the details. As the course progresses, you will come to understand many of the physical principles that govern the Universe.
4. Most of the quantitative parts will be easy to understand if you have a good knowledge of high-school algebra and geometry, as well as some high-school physics. However, if you don't understand them, or are not in the mood for math and physics, you can largely ignore these interludes; just try to get the *qualitative* idea.
5. Some lectures are more technical than others, but they lay the foundations for future lectures, and at least a

qualitative understanding should be accessible to most viewers. Part I of the course, in particular, discusses some of the techniques used by astronomers.

V. In the video lectures, I now gave a brief overview of many of the topics to be covered in the course, and showed an assortment of photographs.

    A. Rather than list them here, however, I suggest that you leaf through the recommended textbooks and look at some of the stunning photographs. Also, a good idea of what the course will cover can be obtained by skimming the summary paragraph for each lecture.

    B. Here I provide a few definitions that will make it easier for you to understand the material in the first few lectures, before some of these topics are discussed in detail.

        1. *Light year*: The distance light travels in one year—about 10 trillion kilometers.

        2. *Star*: A self-luminous, gravitationally bound ball of gas that shines (or used to shine) because of nuclear reactions in its core. The Sun is a typical star.

        3. *Planet*: A body of substantial size (larger than about 1000 kilometers in diameter), but not massive enough for nuclear reactions ever to begin, typically orbiting a star.

        4. *Planetary system*: A collection of planets and smaller bodies orbiting a star.

        5. *Galaxy*: A large (typically 5000 to 200,000 light years in diameter), gravitationally bound system of hundreds of millions (and up to a trillion) stars.

        6. *Quasar*: A star-like, extremely luminous (powerful) object billions of light years away.

        7. *Universe*: "All that there is." (Actually, there could be other, physically disjoint universes with which we have no direct interactions!)

Essential Readings:

The standard textbooks recommended to accompany these video lectures are as follows. These books should be consulted for *all* of the lectures; they will not be repeated in the individual lists of suggested readings.

Pasachoff, J. M. *Astronomy: From the Earth to the Universe*, 5th Edition. Saunders, 1998.

Pasachoff, J. M. *Journey Through the Universe*. Saunders, 1994 version. This is a shorter book than the one above; it concentrates on the fundamentals. A new edition (*The Cosmos: Astronomy in the New Millenium*) will appear in the year 2000, by Jay M. Pasachoff and Alex Filippenko. It is most likely to follow the approximate structure of the video lectures.

Fraknoi, A., Morrison, D., and Wolff, S. *Voyages Through the Universe*. Saunders, 1997.

Several monthly non-technical magazines on astronomy should also be consulted; they have a wealth of useful information about new discoveries, current events in the sky, etc. The best three are *Sky and Telescope* (Sky Pub. Co.; http://www.skypub.com), *Astronomy* (Kalmbach Pub.; http://www.kalmbach.com/astro/astronomy.html), and *Mercury* (Astronomical Society of the Pacific; http://www.aspsky.com).

Viewers who want to see much more mathematics and physics should consult the following textbook: Shu, F. H. *The Physical Universe: An Introduction to Astronomy*. Univ. Science Books, 1982.

The Astronomical Society of the Pacific (ASP) serves as a link between professional astronomers, amateur astronomers, teachers, and the general public. They provide a wide variety of services, and their catalog of astronomical items (t-shirts, posters, slides, puzzles, etc.) is excellent. Many of the slides shown in the video course can be purchased from the ASP through their catalog. You are encouraged to join the ASP. See their Web site at http://www.aspsky.org/.

Questions to Consider:

1. What do *you* hope to get out of this course?

2. In what ways do you think the study of astronomy is an investigation of our origins?

Lecture One—Transcript
A Grand Tour of the Cosmos

Greetings. My name is Alex Filippenko and I'd like to welcome you to this 40-lecture survey course, "Understanding the Universe: An Introduction to Astronomy." This is Lecture One, "A Grand Tour of the Cosmos."

We are now in a golden age of astronomy. Amazing discoveries are being made at a rapid pace with powerful new instruments such as the Hubble Space Telescope and the Keck telescopes. Hardly a week goes by without some sort of astronomical news story. Almost every month there are major headlines in astronomy: the detection of planets around other stars; the birth of stars out of gas and dust; the embryos surrounding them; colossal stellar explosions; the rock; the gas around them; black holes, from which nothing can emerge, not even light; newborn galaxies and the ripples of space-time from which they formed; colliding galaxies and colossal bursts of star formation; the age of the Universe; and the possibility of life elsewhere in the Solar System.

Part of my goal in this course is to share with you the excitement and the magnificence of the Universe. It is a pleasure to have been given this opportunity. For those of you who are brand new to astronomy and just curious about what you've heard and read, I want to introduce you to the major topics to give you a foundation which will allow you to go read articles and watch TV programs about astronomy and more fully comprehend and enjoy them. I'd like to introduce you to some of the most mind-boggling concepts imaginable so that you'll have fun sharing in the mystery of the cosmos.

If you know some astronomy already and like it, I'd like you to become ravenous for the subject. I'd like to share with you the intricate connections between different topics in astronomy—the fact, for example, that we are made of elements that were produced in the colossal explosions of stars long ago. For those of you who are real astronomy buffs, I would like to reinforce and extend your knowledge and share with you some insights to give you some new ideas that you may never have considered before.

In any case, I would like all of you to come away from this course with a lifelong interest in astronomy.

My second goal is to show you that astronomy is basically a story of our origins. How did we get here and where are we going? How did our Milky Way Galaxy form? How did stars form? From where did the elements of which planets and life consists come? What is going to happen to our star, the Sun? What is going to happen to Earth? What is going to happen to the Universe? Are there others out there who may be thinking the same thoughts as we are?

It's possible that many of you have thought about these questions, or at least some of them, while staring out into the dark night sky while camping in the woods, for example. These are natural questions that stem from human curiosity about our place in the Universe. This is perhaps what makes astronomy the most personal of all sciences.

This is a survey course, so I won't go into all the gory details. You can get those later from a more detailed book. Socrates said that education is "the kindling of a flame, not the filling of a vessel," and it is in that spirit that I am giving this course. I hope that you will continue to learn more about the cosmos and our place in it and about our origins. Another of my goals is to show you as much as possible how science works and to convey to you the thrill of scientific discovery, the thrill that drives most scientists to pursue their work with a passion.

Science is a dynamic process; it is not static. Ideas are developed. They are tested with observations and experiments. If they agree with the results of observations, we continue on and try to see whether there are other circumstances in which they agree. But if they fail, we have to revise them. We revise them in such a way as to agree with the largest number of observations and experiments possible. If even one well-executed experiment clearly shows that a theory or hypothesis fails, we must discard or modify the hypothesis; so nothing is taken on faith.

It is this process of science that sets it apart from other ways, no less good perhaps, of looking at the world. It's just a different way of looking at the world, a quantitative way.

Some of the views that I will discuss in this 40-lecture course are at the cutting edge of astronomy. They may not stand the test of time. What I will tell you is the state of our knowledge as of mid-1998. It is conceivable that even a year from now some of what I have said will have been shown to be false, but some of the foundations, I believe, will remain. Newton's laws of motion are so well tested in terrestrial environments that they are unlikely to be discarded. The idea that atoms exist is so well tested that it is unlikely to be discarded. These are the foundations upon which we can build new hypotheses, new theories of how it is the Universe works.

Be prepared when you read the newspapers in a year or two to see changes and differences from what I said. That is part of the fun. It doesn't mean that science has failed. In fact, the whole essence of science is that we are continually revising what it is we think and trying to get a more complete, more correct view of the Universe.

I will try to indicate which parts of the course are the most speculative and which parts sit on a solid foundation, so that you will be able to be on the lookout in the newspapers for parts that might change over time.

I will not in this course use science to conclude why it is we are here. Why do the laws of physics exist? For what purpose were humans placed in the world? I don't think that physics, or science in general; at least the way that we think of it now, can answer those questions. They are better suited to philosophy, theology and metaphysics.

My purpose here will be to show you how it is we determine the laws of physics and how we try to use those laws to explain what we see and to make predictions about new, previously unobserved phenomena. That is the essence of science: to understand how the Universe works, not why it is here.

This will be a visually rich course with lots of photographs from the Hubble Space Telescope and many other modern instruments. I will try, insofar as possible, to describe some of the images so that the audio listeners can gain some appreciation of what I'm discussing. Many of the images can be found in textbooks or in recommended books that I will list in the accompanying notes to this course. I urge you to look at those photographs to gain a full appreciation of what it is I'm discussing.

The course is meant to be mostly descriptive, non-technical and non-mathematical. But astronomy is a physical science, so in addition to the qualitative relationships between things, I will, on some occasions, show you the quantitative relationships. Many of the viewers of The Teaching Company tapes have indicated a desire to see the quantitative foundations of astronomy and physics. I will attempt to show you those in simple terms, but at the same time emphasize the qualitative relationships among objects and quantities. If you don't like the math, or don't feel in the mood for it, or don't understand it, that is okay because it will take up only a small part of the course and you can still enjoy the qualitative relationships that I will discuss. When one thing gets bigger, another gets smaller. Maybe the product of the two remains a constant, but all you really need to know is that when one gets bigger, the other gets smaller—that kind of thing. I think you will still enjoy the course if you follow through the mathematical and technical sections in this manner, listening for the qualitative relationships.

Most of the course will not have any math at all, but some parts are more mathematical than others and the first section of the course in particular, which lays some of the physical foundations, does introduce some of the technical quantities. I think it will not detract from your enjoyment of the course if you ignore these, if you so choose.

I would like now to give you an overview of the entire course to show what it is we'll be studying, and to give you an idea of some of the definitions and terms I'll be using throughout the course. All of these terms will be defined more thoroughly later, at the appropriate time, but when discussing stars it helps to know that stars come in giant collections called galaxies.

First let me show you some of the typical math and physics we'll use. Here is a blackboard full of equations relevant to this course; and if you believe that, then I've got a bridge I can sell you. This is not typical at all of the kind of math I'll be using. I'll be using simple math and sparingly in most lectures. This is just something from Einstein's Theory of Relativity.

I will start the course with an overview of time scales. Time scales in the Universe are very long. We have reason to believe that the Universe is something like 14 billion years old. This comes from the fact that all of the galaxies are moving away from each other at a speed that is proportional to their distance; and if you extrapolate this whole thing backwards in time, you conclude that it is as though the Universe is a gigantic cosmic bomb that went off and has been expanding ever since and is about 14 billion years old.

Our Earth and Moon shown in this image are about 4.5 billion years old, roughly one third of the present age of the Universe. It is as though the Universe lived through two thirds of its current life before the Earth, Moon and the Solar System were formed.

The galaxies are these giant collections of stars. Here's the Andromeda Galaxy. It looks very much like our own Milky Way Galaxy would appear if we could view it from the outside. It's 100,000 light years across. A light year is the distance light travels in a year. It's about 6 trillion miles. This is a huge thing. It is a gravitationally bound collection of hundreds of billions of stars. We live in such a collection.

This particular one is about 2 million light years away, which means that the light that we are now receiving from it left that galaxy about 2 million years ago, before humans were on the face of the Earth. Similarly, they in that galaxy observing us right now, would be seeing us as we were 2 million years ago. So they would not see any homo sapiens.

Astronomers get most of their information about the Universe from light. Here we see a rainbow—white light dispersed by the rain droplets into the component colors. We will see that a quantitative study of those colors tells us about the physical characteristics of the objects that omitted the light. You can tell the kind of chemical composition, the temperature, the distance, and the speed of the object. All sorts of things come from a quantitative analysis of that light.

Because of light's grand importance in astronomy, I will describe in some detail what we believe light is, what is the physical basis of light.

We will see that different elements produce a spectrum, like a rainbow having different characteristic patterns. Here is the pattern due to mercury gas. It differs from the pattern due to sodium gas. Both of those differ from helium. Hydrogen is different still. All of the chemical elements produce different patterns of light. By measuring those patterns in laboratory gases and comparing with the patterns we see in distant parts of the cosmos, we have concluded that essentially all of the cosmos consists of gases of elements that are essentially the same as those that are here on Earth: hydrogen, helium, mercury, sodium, things like that. This is how we know of what substances the Universe is made. It is from this technique of spectroscopy, the quantitative analysis of light.

We collect light with telescopes. Telescopes are like gigantic eyeballs collecting the light raining down from the stars, bringing it to a focus and allowing us to see faint, distant, dim objects in the Universe. If we were to study the Universe with our eyes alone, we would only see the brightest, most nearby stars.

So I will tell you about how telescopes work. Telescopes can collect different types of light and different types of electromagnetic radiation. In this picture, we see an array of radio telescopes, which is used to study the Universe at radio wavelengths (wavelengths that are longer than visible light).

The Hubble Space Telescope, which was launched in 1990, initially had a flaw in its mirror. The corrective optics have now been placed within the telescope, and the resulting data sent back by the Hubble Telescope is astonishing. As I mentioned before, much of what I say in this course of the most modern recent discoveries were made with the Hubble Telescope and complementary telescopes here on the ground. Hubble is up in orbit around the Earth above the effects of Earth's atmosphere, so you get a much clearer view of the Universe with Hubble.

We will then look at certain sky phenomena, such as the seasons. Why are the days longer in the summer and shorter in the winter? Why do the stars appear to rotate across the sky during the course of the night? Why do different people on different parts of the Earth see different patterns of stars? Those sorts of phenomena are everyday phenomena with which all of us are familiar and which can be explained in relatively simple terms.

The stars, of course, are arranged in patterns that we call constellations. Here is Leo the lion. It even looks kind of like a lion. Most constellations do not look like the objects after which they were named. We will see that usually there's no physical relationship among the stars in a given constellation. They just happen to be projected in about the same line of sight, but they're fun to study.

During the course of the Earth's rotation through the night, the stars appear to track circular paths or arcs across the sky. This is a time exposure where a camera was placed on a tripod and the shutter of the camera was opened for many hours allowing the stars to rotate across the sky and as the world turned, they left their arc-like imprints on the emulsion of the film. These sorts of pictures show fairly clearly that the stars circle around a point in the sky called the celestial pole. The farther a star is from the pole, the bigger the circle over which it rotates.

We will next move on to study the Sun, the nearest star. The Sun is so nearby that we can look at it in great detail. The things we learn about the Sun may be generally applicable to other stars. Conversely, we find that certain aspects of the other stars differ from those of the Sun. The Sun is basically a gigantic ball of gas, gravitationally bound together in a sphere 109 times the diameter of Earth itself. So stars are gargantuan balls of gas, and other stars are like that as well, not just the Sun.

The Sun has sunspots on it. These are cooler regions on the surface of the Sun that look dark because they are cooler, and they emit less radiation than the surrounding hotter regions. Those cool regions are produced by tangled magnetic fields. We will encounter magnetic fields throughout the course.

The corona of the Sun is beautifully visible during a solar eclipse. A solar eclipse is one of the most wonderful natural phenomena that I have ever witnessed. If you have never seen a solar eclipse, go out of your way to see it. You will be a changed person. One picture hardly conveys the magnificence of the experience. You have to be there. You have to feel the temperatures changing. You have to see the darkness encroaching upon you. It is an amazing experience, and it teaches us a lot about stars, because the corona of our Sun, a hot tenuous gas, can only be studied during the time of an eclipse.

Lunar eclipses are also beautiful to watch. The adrenalin doesn't flow quite as much because a lunar eclipse lasts for about an hour, whereas a solar eclipse, at least the totality, lasts for only a few minutes. You can't go off and have a beer during a solar eclipse; you'll miss the whole thing. Whereas during a lunar eclipse, you can kick back, watch it at a leisurely pace and enjoy the unfolding of the celestial phenomenon. It occurs when the Moon goes into Earth's shadow.

To understand eclipses, we have to understand the geometrical relationship between the Sun, the Earth and the Moon. That also dictates the phases of the Moon. The crescent phase is not caused by clouds on the Moon or by clouds in the Earth's atmosphere, but rather by the fact that the illuminated portion of the Moon doesn't happen to coincide with the half that we see. We see only a small sliver of the illuminated portion of the Moon in the case of the crescent Moon.

We will then, in Part Two of the course, move on to study our Solar System in more detail. We will look at the formation of our Solar System and how we think it formed from a contracting cloud of gas and dust that was spinning rapidly. We will look at the coalescence of that gas into material bodies called planets.

In the next slide, you can see Aristotle's model of the Solar System. He had Earth at the center, and the earthly elements—earth, air, fire, and water—down here on Earth. In the firmament he had the various planets and the stars, glued like jewels to the celestial sphere, moved around the Earth by the prime mover. This model held on for about two millennia until the Renaissance. It was replaced by Copernicus's heliocentric—that is, Sun-centered—model of the Solar System where the planets orbit the Sun, not the Earth.

This was a revolution. We will see the Copernican revolution reappear later in our study of the Universe when we realize that the stars are simply other suns and that the galaxies are simply other galaxies. We do not appear in any way to be the center of the Universe. That is not to detract from our own importance. To you, in your daily lives, of course, you and your loved ones are the most important things. But in the grand scale of the cosmos, we do not appear to hold a central position.

Perhaps we do hold a central position if we are the only creatures that can ponder the Universe and ask these question, but we don't know the answer to that question yet. Perhaps there are many intelligent civilizations that are asking these very same questions.

The phases of Venus are what showed that the Copernican system—the heliocentric system—is correct and that the Earth-centric system is incorrect. We will see how geometrically one cannot explain the full set of the phases of Venus in the Earth-centered theory of the Solar System. It just cannot be done.

Newton, perhaps the greatest scientist of all time, supposedly looked at an apple falling from a tree as he sat in the countryside away from Cambridge and away from the plague and realized that the Moon was being pulled by Earth's gravity in much the way that the apple was being pulled by Earth's gravity. He tried to unify these two motions—the falling of the apple and the orbit of the Moon around the Earth. In so doing, he invented the Law of Gravitation. He used Galileo's experiments to come up with the three laws of motion that we now know. He revolutionized science forever. His influence will surely be lasting.

We will then go on to study the planets individually, starting with the Earth and moving on. The Earth has many interesting phenomena associated with it: tides, auroras, and the northern and southern lights (the glowing gases that we sometimes see when we are far up north or far down south). We will understand how those phenomena are produced.

We will look at the Moon and the experiments that some of the astronauts did while they were up there. To this day, I cannot help, when looking at the Moon, but feel incredible awe and exhilaration at the fact that humans have actually walked around on that giant gray slab of rock out there and performed experiments which have actually given us clues to the age of the Earth and the process by which the Earth was formed. That is the real value of studying other planets and moons. It gives us insight into the formation of the Earth and the Solar System—our origins.

Venus is shrouded in clouds and at one time was thought to be a rather pleasant place to live. We now know that it is hellishly hot and no water exists on the surface. In the case of Mars we really think it used to be a pleasant place to live. It wasn't just thought it was a pleasant place. We actually really do believe that it was a pleasant place to live at one time in its past. There is evidence of dry riverbeds on the surface of Mars, indicating the presence of liquid, running water. What happened to Mars to make it freeze dried, as it is now?

Venus is too hot. Mars is too cold. The Earth is just right. We should learn from these other two planets and perhaps prevent our own Earth from becoming too hot or too cold to be livable.

There is the possibility of life on Mars. This was announced not even two years ago. The evidence is very controversial and the controversy continues. New evidence is being unearthed—or "un-

Mars-ed", as you may put it—and we don't yet know whether there was ever any primitive life on Mars, but the search will continue.

Jupiter, a gigantic planet, is beautiful in that it has a very complex atmosphere and many moons, two of which are shown here. One of the moons, Io, looks like a pizza. Here it is. It has an extremely volcanically active surface. It has several dozen volcanoes or hot spots going on at the same time, much more active than the Earth. Why is that the case? We will come to understand that.

Saturn, with its magnificent rings is, to me, the most beautiful planet because at the age of 12 or 13, I independently discovered Saturn. No one told me to look at it. I just happened to look at it through a telescope about the same size as the one we see here. I stumbled upon it, and it knocked my socks off because I realized what a thrill it is to discover something. Maybe millions of people had seen Saturn before me, but that was okay because I had discovered it for myself. I realized then what the thrill of discovery really means and what the feeling is really like.

Then we will discuss the debris of the solar system, the asteroids, which are chunks of rock left over that didn't make a planet, or are perhaps a planet that broke up, and comets—primitive frozen, dirty ice balls that were formed early in the history of the Solar System and then ejected to large distances from the Sun. Occasionally they come back, and the sunlight evaporates them and causes the gases to be pushed back. It's those gases that reflect sunlight that produce the tail.

Sometimes meteors are formed in the Earth's atmosphere from little chunks of rock—asteroids and comets that may have broken apart. If a whole comet broke apart and we encountered the clump of debris, we could have an intense meteor shower, as is shown in this picture—dozens of meteors within a span of just a few tens of seconds. This was an exceptional meteor shower. Another one like it, we hope, is coming up in 1999.

Occasionally this debris slams into planets. Here is the debris from Comet Shoemaker-Levy 9 smashing into the planet Jupiter. The energy released by one of the 20 fragments that hit Jupiter is 100,000 times greater than that released by the most powerful explosives that we have ever built here on Earth. Had even one of those fragments, let alone the entire comet, hit the Earth, the consequences for human life would have been devastating. We have evidence that this has occurred in the past. It will probably again occur in the future. It behooves us to understand this process and to search the heavens for projectiles that might be heading our way, lest we suffer the same fate as the dinosaurs did 65 million years ago when one of these giant comets is believed to have crashed into the Earth.

We will then go on to study the stars. Here is Comet Hale Bopp among the stars. Thankfully, when it came by in 1997, it didn't come anywhere close to the earth, so there was no danger of it hitting. But, mark my words, there is a comet or an asteroid out there somewhere heading our way some day. Hopefully not before next Tuesday or Wednesday, maybe even not before next year, but someday this will happen to us.

Looking at the stars, we see that they have different degrees of brightness and different colors. The degrees brightness are due to their intrinsic powers and their distances. Those two quantities dictate the brightness of the star. The color is a measure of the temperature of the star, in particular, of the star's outermost part.

Stars form from giant clouds of gas and dust called nebulae. This is the Orion nebula. In the central region, here, you can see a cluster of stars that formed relatively recently on the cosmic scale, just a few million years ago as compared with our 4.5 billion years for the age of the Solar System and the Sun. Stars often form in clusters; they seem to be social creatures, not because they think about it, but that's just the way gravity operates.

The clusters of stars can teach us all sorts of things about how stars age and how they die. We find, in fact, from studies of bound pairs of stars that almost everything about a star is dictated by its initial mass. We can determine the masses of binary stars by using Newton's laws of motion and gravitation. If we measure the masses, and we see what the characteristics of the stars are, we find that, in fact, the characteristics are dictated by the mass. The mass pretty much determines what a star is going to look like and even how long it will live. Most of us don't know how long we will live, but a star of a given mass, if it had a brain, would know how long it would live if it knew its mass.

The dying stages of a star like our Sun look something like this. Through a series of cosmic burps—relatively non-violent ejections—

our Sun in about six or seven billion years will throw out its outer atmosphere of gases much like this star did. What will remain in the center is a retired star. We call it a white dwarf. It's very small. It's about the size of the Earth. Here's an example. Sirius B is a white dwarf, much smaller than our Sun and about the size of the Earth. It's made out of a weird sort of matter known as degenerate matter, not because it's morally reprehensible but simply because this is the term that quantum physicists have given to this peculiar state of matter.

We will study how some stars violently explode at the ends of their lives. Our own Sun will not go through this kind of violence but some stars do; and it is this sort of explosion that propels chemically enriched gases into the cosmos. The gases were enriched through nuclear fusion during the normal life of the star and through nuclear fusion during the explosion. If those gases are then propelled into space by these colossal explosions, they mix with the gases that are already present among and between the stars. They can then contract and form new stars, chemically enriched stars, stars that might have rocky planets such as the Earth and Mars orbiting them.

We are the stuff of stars. I will show you how the heavy elements in our bodies came from the explosions of stars long ago.

Some of these explosions leave bizarre remnants called neutron stars. Here's one blinking at us; here it's on, there it's off. There you have about the mass of the Sun compressed into a volume about the size of a city maybe 10 or 15 kilometers in radius, a tiny volume but a huge mass. This is like one gigantic atomic nucleus.

Even more bizarre is the remnant left behind by some stars, the black hole, which according to Einstein's general relativity theory is bent or curved so much that nothing, not even light, can escape. In the Newtonian view it is simply the fact that gravity is so strong that no matter how fast you throw a ball, that ball can't escape. Even light can't escape, and that is where the relativity comes in, because Newton's laws do not necessarily imply that light can't escape, but Einstein's equations do. They suggest that black holes really are black. They are pits in space-time from which nothing can occur.

Here is my prize-winning photo of a black hole taken with the lens cap on my camera lens, so there you go. If anyone wants to pay me $10,000 for that picture, I'll be glad to take your money.

Black holes, we think, do exist. Whether they join different universes or different parts of our Universe to each other through passages called wormholes is not yet known. Mathematically, it seems as though one black hole can join another black hole in another Universe—whatever that means, and I'll define it later—or to another part of our Universe. Maybe one can take a short cut through that wormhole. We actually think that's not the case, but at least some of the aspects of the mathematics seem to imply that.

We will then move on to a study of galaxies (collections of stars). Our own galaxy, the Milky Way—and here you can see why it's called the Milky Way—consists of about 400 billion stars gravitationally bound to each other. There are other galaxies like our own, spiral galaxies, in whose spiral arms you see nebulae like this Orion nebula. These nebulas light up the spiral arms of spiral galaxies and cause those arms to glow. There are lots of nebulae like the Orion nebula in these arms. There are lots of young, massive, very hot, very luminous stars. We would like to understand how galaxies form.

One clue comes from the fact that stars in galaxies move around very quickly. They're just zipping along back and forth. To produce the observed amount of motion, we conclude that there must be a tremendous amount of dark material within these galaxies. The observed light is not all that there is. There's dark material as well, and it influences the formation and the structure of a galaxy.

If we look at giant clusters of galaxies, gravitationally bound conglomerations of galaxies, we again see evidence for large amounts of dark matter. We can't see the dark matter directly, but we can tell it's there because of its gravitational influence.

If we look at galaxies that are many billions of light years away, they are seen as they were billions of years ago. Light travels with a finite speed, so if we look at something that is five billion years in the past, it is seen as it was when the Universe was much younger. We can draw inferences about what our own galaxy may have looked like in the past by looking at these very distant galaxies. You can see they look quite peculiar, not as regular as beautiful large spirals like our own Milky Way. Maybe this is what our own Milky Way looked like in the distant past.

Some galaxies in the distant past were very bright. This is not a star. It is actually the center of a galaxy, but it looks like a star. The center of this galaxy is so brilliant that we think that an enormous black hole is swallowing huge amounts of material in that galaxy. Before the material enters the black hole, it can emit light. Of course, it doesn't shine after it gets within the black hole, but while it's still outside the black hole, it can shine. It shines in a very efficient way, and this is what we think produces the light of quasars. We actually have direct evidence now for gigantic black holes in the centers of galaxies that presumably used to be quasars.

When we look at the sky very deeply, we find that it consists mostly of galaxies. This is the Hubble Space Telescope Deep Field. It is the deepest picture ever taken of the Universe. Most of the blotches you see here are collections of tens and hundreds of billions of stars. They are not stars in our own galaxy. Here's a star in our own galaxy. Maybe there are one or two in this picture. I can't find them. Almost all of these are other galaxies.

With so many galaxies in the sky—perhaps a hundred billion—and with hundreds of billions of stars per galaxy, it's natural to ask, "Is there any life out there?" "Are there any planets out there?" We see evidence for the formation of planets around other stars. We see disks of gas and dust around newborn or newly forming stars, which may well coalesce into planets. So we think there are planets out there.

Is there life? Among the planets that have been discovered so far, we don't know of any direct evidence for life. Here are the planets around other stars that are known so far, but our technology is still primitive. We're still looking. We're still listening, like with this gigantic radio telescope in Puerto Rico. We're listening to the heavens to see if we can detect any sort of intelligent or intelligible radio transmissions that are coming from other civilizations out there. Maybe they are trying to communicate with us in the same way that we have been sending signals into outer space, either intentionally, in some cases, or inadvertently with our radio and television channels.

Some may say that we not only have evidence for life out there, we have evidence for intelligent life, and maybe it's even here on Earth. After all, here's a reputable publication that announces that there are five U.S. senators who are space aliens. Obviously, you should not believe absolutely everything you read, especially in certain reputable journals or disreputable journals. Find out if your senator is on the list.

We will end the course with cosmology, the study of the origin, structure and evolution of the Universe as a whole. When you look out at the dark sky, one of the simplest yet profound questions you can ask is, "Why is the sky dark?" "Why isn't it bright?" You might say, "What a crazy dude from Berkeley! The sky is dark at night because the Sun went down, dingbat!" It sounds like a simple, crazy question, but in fact, it is a very profound question because if the Universe were infinite and there were stars all over the place, eventually every single line of sight would intercept a star and the sky in fact should be brighter than the daytime sky because everywhere there would be suns.

The solution to this paradox is profound. There are several possible solutions, and I will discuss with you those solutions, and I will discuss with you the one that we favor these days.

I mentioned that when we look at distant galaxies and clusters of galaxies, we see them rushing away from us as though the Universe began with a gigantic explosion, the Big Bang. We can calculate the time since that Big Bang. We think it's about 14 billion years, just extrapolating the expansion backwards in time. We can also calculate an age of the Universe by looking at its oldest contents. The Universe had better be at least as old as the oldest thing in it.

This is a globular cluster. The oldest globular clusters are thought to be about 13 or 14 billion years old. Unfortunately, a few years ago, the expansion age determined by some astronomers was only 8 to 12 billion years, shorter than the known ages of the globular clusters—a crisis in the cosmos, or more correctly, a crisis for us. I will show you how we think this crisis has now at least been partially resolved.

We will then look at the global geometry of the Universe. Is it flat like a Euclidean plane? Is it spherically shaped? Or is it more shaped like a saddle? It turns out that any of these possibilities could be out there. We live in one of these universes. In one of these universes, early fluctuations in the amount and density of matter led to the creation of galaxies and clusters of galaxies. These are the shadows of creation, the early clumps of matter from which our galaxy formed.

Our Universe is thought to have inflated very quickly in its earliest few tiny fractions of a second from a sphere smaller than a proton to an enormous vast size, like a bubble growing to an enormous vast size. I'll tell you why we think that was the case. Long in the future, if the bubble keeps on growing, the stars will die out one-by-one, and eventually life as we know, it will be impossible in the Universe because there will be no more stars. It will just all be ice, coldness and darkness.

From where did the Universe form? It may have formed from nothing. Here on your TV screen, you see nothing. How is that possible, you might ask? It could all have been a quantum fluctuation. I'll carefully define what I mean by that. The Universe may have been the ultimate free lunch. Not only that, but it could have happened multiple times. Separate bubbles could have formed or bubbles could have formed within bubbles that branched out, and there could be a whole range of universes. All these bulbous things are universes, detached from our own. It is conceivable that ours is not the only universe, the ultimate extension of the Copernican principle of mediocrity.

In many of the universes, the laws of physics may be such as to not allow life or even have the elements to develop. We are fortunate to live in one that does allow this. Perhaps most are stillborn. They do not allow complexity.

But here we are on Earth, able to ponder these questions. I want to bring you these questions and at least our partial answers throughout this course. I want to bring you astronomy, share with you the excitement and hopefully make it for you a lifelong passion.

Lecture Two
Journey Through Space and Time

Scope:

Various lines of evidence suggest that the Universe was born about 14 billion years ago. One can identify many significant events in the history of the Universe; here we examine seven of these that were critical to the existence of humans. Vast distances in the Universe are most easily considered in terms of the time it takes light to traverse them. For example, stars visible to the unaided eye are typically hundreds of light years away, whereas galaxies viewed through large telescopes can be billions of light years away. The finite speed of light allows us to see distant objects as they were in the past; thus, we can "look back in time" and study the evolution of the Universe. To gain a complete understanding of the Universe, astronomers must also study atoms and subatomic particles. As with many physical concepts, a better intuitive feel for the range of distances in the Universe can be gained through the use of scale models.

Objectives

Upon completion of this lecture, you should be able to:

1. Explain how the finite speed of light allows us to look back in time, thereby getting a direct view of the Universe early in its evolution.

2. Describe several key events (and their times) in the history of the Universe.

3. Construct a scale model of the Universe that illustrates the relative distances and sizes of various objects.

4. Use ratios and proportions to simplify many types of problems and to illustrate general relationships.

5. Express quantities in terms of scientific notation, and solve simple algebraic problems with the correct units.

Outline

I. A brief overview of scientific notation, common prefixes, and units may be useful.

  A. It is cumbersome to write down and keep track of lots of zeros, so astronomers use *scientific notation* (also known as exponential notation).

1. The basic idea is to express a quantity as a number between 1 and 10, multiplied by 10 raised to some integer (power.)
2. Numbers like 150,000,000 are written as 1.5×10^8, because you need to move *eight* spaces to the *right* of the decimal point in 1.5 to get 150,000,000.
3. The number 0.0000158, on the other hand, is written as 1.58×10^{-5}, because you need to move *five* spaces to the *left* of the decimal point in 1.58 to get 0.0000158. In fact, 10^{-5} is just $1/10^5$, or 0.00001, and we have simply multiplied this by 1.58.

B. Common prefixes are kilo (k; $1000 = 10^3$), centi (c; $1/100 = 0.01 = 10-2$), and milli (m; $1/1000 = 0.001 = 10-3$). Astronomers also use mega (M; 106), giga (G; 109), micro (μ; 10-6), and nano (n; 10-9).

C. In this lecture series we will generally use the *metric system*.
1. The unit of length is the meter (m). One meter is 39.37 inches, a bit larger than a yard.
2. The unit of mass is the gram (g). There are 453.6 grams in one pound.
3. The unit of time is the second (s).
4. Temperatures will be given on the absolute (Kelvin) scale, in which the lowest possible temperature is 0 K. Degrees Kelvin = degrees Celsius (C) + 273. Degrees Fahrenheit (F) = (9/5)C + 32.

II. The history of the Universe spans a vast amount of time and contains at least seven steps critical to the existence of humans.

A. The Universe began roughly 14 billion years ago in an "explosion" known as the Big Bang.
1. Clusters of galaxies are moving away from each other, and the speed of recession is proportional to distance. Extrapolation of the expansion backward in time suggests that the density was infinite 14 billion years ago.
2. There is radiation left over from the initial hot phase of the Universe.
3. Helium, synthesized from hydrogen during the first 3 minutes, is found in nearly uniform quantities throughout the Universe.

B. Many galaxies, such as our own Milky Way Galaxy, formed about 13 billion years ago.

    1. The oldest globular star clusters in galaxies appear to be this old.

    2. The oldest elliptical galaxies appear to be this old.

C. The Solar System formed about 4.6 billion years ago.

    1. Radioactive dating of meteorites gives such ages.

    2. Radioactive dating of moon rocks gives ages up to 4.4 billion years, a bit less than 4.6 billion years since it took some time for the initially molten material to solidify.

D. Simple, unicellular life formed at least 3.5 billion years ago.

    1. Fossils indicating the presence of such cells have been found in ancient rocks.

    2. Since such primitive cells produce fossils that are difficult to find and recognize, life may have arisen even earlier than 3.5 billion years ago. Indeed, there is indirect evidence for life 3.8 billion years ago.

E. A number of major jumps occurred in the evolution of life on Earth. One of the most important of these was the Cambrian explosion about 550 million years ago.

    1. There was an enormous diversification of life at this time.

    2. Fossils of large numbers of complex, hard-bodied animals (e.g., trilobites) have been found from this era.

F. Dinosaurs suffered a sudden extinction 65 million years ago, after inhabiting the planet for about 180 million years.

    1. Fossils of dinosaurs are found in strata dating back to about 245 million years ago.

    2. The layers of rock containing dinosaur bones have a relatively sharp boundary dating back to 65 million years ago.

G. The first humans appeared about 350,000 years ago.

    1. The oldest skeletons of *Homo sapiens* date back to this time.

    2. Early hominids such as *Australopithecus*, direct ancestors of humans, appeared earlier—about 3.5 million years ago.

III. To place astronomical time scales into perspective, one can suppose that the entire 14 billion year history of the Universe were compressed into one 24-hour day (86,400 seconds).

    A. In this model, the Earth formed about 8 hours ago, because the ratio 4.6 billion to 14 billion is roughly the same as the ratio 8 hours to 24 hours.

    B. Similarly, humans appeared only about 2 seconds ago. A human lifetime of 100 years is only 0.0006 s, or 6 ten-thousandths of a second!

IV. Astronomical distance scales also span an enormous range.

    A. The average distance between the Sun and the Earth is 150 million kilometers (1.5×10^8 km), or 93 million miles (since 1 km $\approx$ 0.6 mile).

        1. This is known as the "Astronomical Unit" (A.U.).

        2. Stars, and especially galaxies, are *much* farther away than an A.U.

    B. A convenient way to give very large distances is in terms of the *light travel time.*

        1. The speed of light in a vacuum, 3×10^5 km/s (or 186,000 miles per second), is constant. It is the largest possible speed with which information can travel through space.

        2. If speed is constant, then distance equals speed multiplied by time ($d = vt$). Thus, solving for time, we have $t = d/v$, and for light this becomes $t = d/c$.

        3. Light traveling from the Moon, 3.84×10^5 km away, takes $t = (3.84 \times 10^5 \text{ km})/(3 \times 10^5 \text{ km/s}) = 1.3$ seconds (s) to reach us. We say that the Moon is "1.3 light seconds away." This led to the noticeable delay in the responses of lunar astronauts to (radio transmitted) questions from people on Earth.

        4. Since $t = d/c = (1/c)d$, we say that the light travel time is *proportional* to distance, and $(1/c)$ is the constant of proportionality.

        5. The Sun is 390 times farther from Earth than the Moon is. Hence, light from the Sun takes $(1.3 \text{ s})(390) = 500$ s to reach us. This is 8.3 minutes, since 1 minute = 60 seconds.

6. We say that the Sun is "8.3 light minutes away." If the Sun abruptly stopped shining, we wouldn't know it for 8.3 minutes because the emitted light is already on its way!

7. A *light year* (ly) is the distance light travels in one year: $d = (3 \times 10^5 \text{ km/s})(1 \text{ year})$. Converting 1 year into seconds, we have (1 year)(365.25 days/year)(24 hours/day)(60 minutes/hour)(60 seconds/minute) = 3.15×10^7 seconds, so $d = 9.6 \times 10^{12}$ km, about *10 trillion km* (i.e., 6 trillion miles)!

8. The nearest star, Proxima Centauri (a companion of α [alpha] Centauri), is 4.3 ly away. Other stars visible in the night sky are tens, hundreds, or even thousands of light years away. Thus, different stars are seen at *different times in the past.*

9. The nearest large collection of stars, the Andromeda galaxy, is over 2 million ly away (and about 100 thousand ly in diameter). Galaxies are typically millions of ly apart.

10. The faint light just now reaching us from distant galaxies many billions of ly away allows us to see them as they were billions of years ago.

11. Quasars are not seen nearby; they are always billions of ly away. They appear to be an early stage in the formation of some galaxies.

12. Hence, the finite speed of light gives us a "fossil record" of the Universe's history. If we assume that distant parts of the Universe are fundamentally similar to nearby parts, we can gain insights into how our own cosmic environment may have evolved.

C. Astronomers must also consider objects on tiny scales, such as atoms and subatomic particles.

1. The physical properties of subatomic particles help determine the overall structure of the Universe on large scales.

2. Atoms emit and absorb light, thereby allowing us to study distant objects.

3. A hydrogen atom is roughly 5×10^{-11} meter (m) in radius, as defined by the probable location of the electron.

4. The nucleus (proton) of a hydrogen atom is 10^{-15} m in radius, 50 thousand times smaller than the electron distance. Thus, although it appears opaque, a solid object consists almost entirely of empty space!

V. Scale models can help put all of these distances into perspective.

   A. Suppose the *Sun,* 1.4×10^6 km in diameter (about 110 times the diameter of the Earth), were only the size of the period at the end of this sentence (about 0.5 mm).

      1. A star 5 ly away would be at a distance of 16 km in this model!

      2. The Milky Way Galaxy, about 10^5 ly in diameter, would be 320,000 km in size—not quite the distance to the Moon.

   B. Now suppose a hydrogen *atom* were the diameter of an apple, about 8 cm.

      1. On this scale, a human (20 billion times larger) would be 1.6 million km high—over four times the distance to the Moon!

      2. Nevertheless, the nucleus (proton) of the atom would be only 1.6 *millionths* of a meter (i.e., 1.6μm) in diameter.

Essential Readings:

Sagan, C. *Cosmos*. Random House, 1980.

Morrison, Philip., Morrison, Phylis., and The Office of Charles and Ray Eames. *Powers of 10*. Scientific American Library, 1982. A video version is also available.

Questions to Consider:

1. How would our view of the Universe differ if the speed of light were infinite?

2. Construct a scale model of our Solar System by choosing a specific object to represent the Sun or the Earth. Consult a standard textbook for a data table of sizes and distances.

3. Which is larger: the ratio of the radius of a hydrogen atom to the radius of a proton, or the ratio of Earth's distance from the Sun to the Sun's radius?

Lecture Two—Transcript
Journey Through Space and Time

As we saw in the introductory lecture, we're going to be dealing with some very large and very small numbers in this course—some gargantuan numbers to describe the sizes of galaxies and the scale of the Universe—and tiny numbers to describe the structure of atoms and subatomic particles, things that will dictate the way in which the Universe behaves.

It's hard to carry around all those zeros. In this slide, you can see the number 10,000. That's a fairly small "large" number, and you might say it's fairly easy to keep track of all those zeros. Later we'll get to very large numbers where it's not so easy, so we might as well express them in what's called "scientific notation", or "exponential notation". That idea, if you haven't seen this before, is to simply write a number as a number between 1 and 10—in this case, 10,000 is 1.0—times 10 to some exponent. In this case, the exponent is 4 because one has to move the decimal point over four places and fill in the blanks with zeros in order to convert 1.0×10^4 into the written number 10,000. In this case, we might as well leave out the 1.0 part and just call it 10^4; so, 10,000 written in scientific notation, is 10^4.

Here is an example: 150,000,000 (150 million), where it start becomes more obvious as to why we'd like to keep track of all these zeros in a simple way; 150 million is, for example, the number of kilometers that is the distance between the Earth and the Sun. It's about 93 million miles, 150 million kilometers. That then can be written as 1.5×10^8 because we move the decimal point over eight spaces, filling in the blanks with zeros, in order to reproduce the written out number 150,000,000.

Moving on to an even bigger number, this is 9,500,000,000,000 (9.5 trillion). It turns out to be roughly the number of kilometers in a light year. I'll define what a light year is in a minute. You can write that number as 9.5×10^{12}; again, because it takes 12 spaces to bring the decimal point over to the very end of the number.

In a similar way, you can describe small numbers with scientific notation. Here is 0.001, 1/1000. That can be written as 1.0×10^{-3}, because you have to go backwards to the left three spaces in order to reproduce this number as it is written out. Now, we can just write this as 10^{-3} and drop the 1. It's useful to know that any number raised to a negative exponent is simply one over that number raised to the corresponding positive exponent. So, 10^{-3} is simply $1/10^3$ or $1/1000$.

Now, taking a much smaller number; this one I won't even read out what it is, 0.0000158. That's 1.58×10^{-5}, because you have to move the decimal point over to the left five spaces in order to reproduce the number as written longhand.

A good example of why we would really like to use scientific notation is when we consider a number like 10^{-43}. Now, you might wonder, why would we ever want to consider a number like 10^{-43}? It turns out that our laws of physics, as we know them right now, can be used to describe the properties of the Universe all the way down to something like 10^{-43} seconds after the Universe began. Before that time, there is some sort of quantum foam, which I'll describe later. We have no real understanding of the laws of physics in that foam.

It's reasonable to discuss the age of the Universe at a time of 10^{-43} seconds. If you were to write that out longhand, you'd fill up all your space with zeros and you'd lose track of some of them, for sure. So we might as well write it as 10^{-43} as an exponent there. That's scientific notation.

The other things we want to be familiar with are the prefixes that will be used in this class, and most of them are probably familiar to you. Kilo is a thousand, or 10^3, like a kilogram (roughly 2.2 pounds). Centi is one one-hundredth, or 10^{-2} or $1/10^2$ or $1/100$. These are all different ways of saying the same thing. Milli is one one-thousandth, or .0001 or 10^{-3}.

There are others that you might be not quite as familiar with, but which are very useful in astronomy and physics. Mega means million, or 10^6. Giga is 10^9, or a billion. We'll be talking about billions of stars. We'll be talking about some giga numbers of stars.

Then, on the small scale, there's micro, which is 10^{-6}, or one one-millionth. So, a micrometer is one one-millionth of a meter. Then on even smaller scales there is nano, which is 10^{-9}, or one one-billionth. It turns out that the sizes of atoms are well described by numbers that are something like a nanometer, or a little bit smaller. Those are prefixes.

The units that I'll typically use in this course are in the metric system. Astronomers use a whole combination of units, and I will not apologize for this too much. I'll introduce some special units, which are very useful for astronomy later on, but in general for familiar quantities, I'll be using the metric system. In the metric system, length is given in meters and a meter is roughly 39.37 inches, or roughly a yard. A kilometer, of course, would be a thousand meters, and that's about 0.6 of a mile. A centimeter is 1/100 of a meter, and it's about 0.39 of an inch. There are 2.54 centimeters per inch.

The unit of mass that we'll use is the gram. There are 454 grams per pound. A kilogram is a thousand grams, and roughly 2.2 pounds. Time, of course, is measured in seconds. That's typical.

Temperature will be measured on the absolute scale, the Kelvin scale, where zero degree is the lowest possible temperature. In principal, all motion ceases at zero degree. Temperature is simply a measure of how quickly atoms, molecules and particles are jiggling around inside something. The temperature of this room is a measure of how quickly the molecules are jiggling around. In principal, at absolute zero, the jiggling stops.

To convert between Kelvin and Celsius, you just add 273 to Celsius in order to get Kelvin. If you want to convert from Celsius to Fahrenheit, you multiply the Celsius temperature by 9/5 and add 32. These relationships are just given here for completeness. We will rarely need to really use this. But, if I give a temperature on the Kelvin scale, you might want to know what it is on the Fahrenheit or the Celsius scale, so here are the formulas.

Now I want to discuss time scales in the Universe. I want to define seven fairly critical times as far as the existence of life on Earth is concerned. Now one can actually define many times that were critical in the history of the Universe for the emergence of humans, but I would choose seven of them, in order to not spend too long a time discussing this.

The first time scale is the age of the Universe. The Universe, we believe, was born at a particular instant in time, about 14 billion years ago. So, the Universe is not 100 billion years old. It is not infinitely old; it is about 14 billion years old. How do we know that? We will discuss this in detail later on, but here in this image, you can see a cluster of galaxies. You can see about a dozen galaxies that form a gravitationally bound cluster. It turns out that when we look at such galaxies of stars, we find that they are moving away from us.

I mentioned this in my introductory lecture. In fact, the more distant ones are moving away faster than the less distant ones. If you think about that, it resembles an explosion. It's as though you have a giant ball exploding and different bits of the ball were given different speeds, and after a given amount of time, the fastest ones went a greater distance than the slow ones. We can extrapolate this backwards in time and come to an approximation of the age of the Universe.

We have other indications that the Universe is not infinitely old. The Universe is bathed in radiation left over from a hot compressed dense state—the so-called Big Bang—and we can actually detect that radiation; there is no other explanation for it. Moreover, the abundance of the lightest elements in the Universe, like hydrogen and helium and the different forms in which they come, are pretty uniform no matter where you look in the Universe, as though they are primordial. Something produced them in the beginning with about the same quantities everywhere, and now we are just seeing all these elements. In stars, we are seeing other heavier elements being built up, and I'll talk about that later. That occurs at different rates in different parts of the Universe, but the amounts of hydrogen and helium are roughly the same everywhere. That suggests that it was primordial. Indeed, it is very reasonable to see how these elements were produced in a hot compressed big bang. So, we believe the Universe does have a finite age, and it is about 14 billion years.

At some point galaxies and stars formed. Here you see a so-called globular cluster. These objects formed about a billion years or so after the Big Bang. Meteorites can be used to determine the age of the Solar System, so the Solar System had to have formed after stars formed, and the stars had to have formed after the Universe formed. The Solar System, being about 4.5 billion years old, is roughly one-third of the age of the Universe.

So, the Universe was two-thirds of its present age when our Solar System formed. This is actually relevant, because it turns out that you need a fair amount of time for the build up of the heavy elements in order for things like rocks, meteorites and the Earth to have formed. The Universe began almost entirely with hydrogen and helium and it took some time for these heavier elements to form.

The next time step that we can consider is the formation of life. In this image, you can see conglomerations of single-cell creatures.

These are fossilized and are called stromatolites. They are colonies of single-celled creatures. Dating of these creatures suggests that the fossils are billions of years old. In the image we have here, these particular ones come from an era about 2.5 billion years ago. But, the oldest single cell creatures that have been found are something like 3.5 billion years old. That is, the fossil evidence for them dates back from 3.5 billion years ago.

These objects, these single-celled creatures, had the consistency of Jello. They had no hard skeleton. They had no hard tubes within them. They were like Jello, or glutinous stuff. It is hard to form a fossil out of such an object, so the fact that we've actually found fossils 3.5 billion years old suggests that life actually started before that, because we probably have not found the oldest fossils, given that they are so difficult to recognize. Indeed, there are indirect arguments that suggest that life on Earth formed 3.8 billion years ago, not too long after the formation of the Earth and the Solar System. Life arising in the cosmos, or at least on Earth, was certainly an important step in our own evolution.

In this picture, you see a trilobite. This is a complex, hard-bodied creature. Many such creatures suddenly burst forth on Earth around 550 million years ago during a time known as the Cambrian explosion. Prior to 550 million years ago, there weren't such hard-bodied creatures. There were mostly these single-celled animals with no real skeleton and nothing really to grab onto, and these fossils were difficult to form. But around 550 million years ago, lots of these trilobites and other hard-bodied animals formed, and the amount of complexity of life on Earth increased by a substantial amount. Something happened after 3 billion years of life, being in a fairly primitive state on Earth. Something happened to raise the level of life to a much higher level of complexity, and that was certainly very significant for the development of humans.

We all know that dinosaurs roamed the Earth for well over 100 million years, actually approaching 200 million years. They were amazingly successful animals. There weren't that many of them, and those that were around, individually, didn't have very long lives. The dinosaurs themselves, overall, had very long lives. As I say, they were around for nearly 200 million years, so they were a very successful type of organism. It's conceivable that we would not be here if the dinosaurs did not somehow perish from the face of the

Earth. There is reasonably good evidence now that the dinosaurs, or at least the last of them, perished in a rather sudden catastrophic event. Some sort of major calamity on Earth killed off the last of the dinosaurs. There is debate as to whether they were on their way out already anyway, but that's beside the point.

We have evidence there was a huge calamity, in part because small creatures, such as these foraminifera, are found in abundance in certain layers or strata of Earth. Then, suddenly, creatures of this particular size and shape are not apparent at all, and in the strata above them there are none whatsoever. So, it's as if most species living at a particular time were destroyed in a very sudden event, and that event was about 65 million years ago. It's called the Cretaceous-Tertiary Extinction, and with it we think the last of the dinosaurs disappeared as well. Regardless of whether you believe that the dinosaurs were on their way out already, we know that a certain calamity occurred on Earth because two-thirds of the little creatures died out as well, in a very sudden way. That perhaps gave room for mammals and other forms of life to become more dominant on the face of the Earth than they had been prior to that time.

Humans (*Homo sapiens*) came around 350,000 years ago. Their ancestors, *Australopithecus* and other hominids, date back to maybe two or three million years ago, but *Homo sapiens* date back to something like 350,000 years ago—quite recent on the cosmic scale of the Earth. If you compress, for example, the 14 billion year history of the Earth into one day, the Earth (4.5 billion years old) formed about eight hours before the end of the day, but humans came around only two seconds ago. Two seconds ago, out of a 24-hour day, humans made their appearance in this Universe. A human lifetime of 100 years is only 6/10,000 of a second of this 24-hour day.

That kind of analogy gives you some appreciation for how long cosmic time scales are and how long even the Earth's time scale is. The Earth has been around for about eight hours out of this day; humans have been around for two seconds, and a lifetime is only 6/10,000 of a second. These are the kinds of timescales that we will be considering in this course.

Let me move on now to distance scales. Here you see the setting Sun. The Sun, as I mentioned, is 150 million kilometers away (93 million miles, if you prefer that). That's a number that is pretty hard for most of us to imagine. What is 150 million kilometers? Few of us can imagine a million of anything. If anyone wants to give me a million dollars, I'll be happy to look at the giant pile of coins and dollars and try to imagine what it looks like; 150 million is even harder to imagine, especially for the stars, which are far more distant than the Sun. We need a better unit of distance, one that is more readily comprehensible and doesn't involve such large numbers. You will see that the stars and the galaxies are almost immeasurably farther away than the Sun, and 150 million is not even a very good number for the Sun.

Let's actually use a very useful concept, and that is the concept of light travel time. The speed of light in a vacuum is the largest possible speed with which information can travel. If I want to send you a message, I can use a carrier pigeon, I can use Federal Express, or I can use light. Light will be the fastest way in which I can transmit a message from one place to another. It travels with a constant speed. So it is natural, especially in the emptiness of space, to consider light as being the carrier of signals and the time light has taken to carry those signals from stars to us.

Let's think in distances in terms of the time it has taken for light to travel from one object to another. For example, you are sitting perhaps 10 feet away from me. Light travels about one foot per nanosecond. One foot per billionth of a second—it is kind of a fun number with which to amaze your friends. So, I'm seeing you as you were 10 billionths of a second ago, because you are about 10 feet away from me, and it took 10 billionths of a second for the light from you to reach me.

I'm seeing someone 50 feet away, 50 billionths of a second ago, and maybe they looked different back then. Well, they didn't. They look about the same, so you might think this is a bit silly to discuss such short distances in terms of light travel time, and it is a bit silly. But I'm leading up to an example of where it's not so silly. If we take distance to be speed times time on this slide, we can rearrange it and see that time is just distance over speed, or distance over the speed of light, if the speed that we're discussing is the speed of light.

Let's consider as another example the time it takes for light to go from the Moon to Earth. The Moon reflects sunlight and then it takes some time to travel between the Moon and the Earth. Looking at this slide, we see that time is distance over speed.

$$t = d/c$$

The distance to the Moon is about 384,000 kilometers. The speed of light is 300,000 kilometers per second (186,000 miles per second). If you divide those two numbers, you get 1.3 seconds. So, we say that the Moon is about 1.3 light seconds away. It takes light 1.3 seconds to reach us from the Moon.

Again, you might not think that that is a very useful quantity, because that is such a nearby distance that we can conceive of it in ways, other than the light travel time. But consider this; here is the Moon. You're seeing it as it was 1.3 seconds ago. A practical application of this is when the astronauts landed on the Moon in 1969. Here you can see Neal Armstrong's boot stepping on the Moon for the first time, and then he walked onto the Moon and Mission Control said, "How does it feel, Neal, to be on the Moon?" A fairly long pause went by and then he said something like, "Great! It feels great to be on the Moon." You wondered, "Why does it take him several seconds to decide that it feels great to be on the Moon? Is he oxygen-starved, like people in the mountains? Is he so in awe of the Moon that he can't think?" No, it's that the radio signal that transmitted the question "How does it feel, Neal, to be on the Moon?" took 1.3 seconds to reach Neal Armstrong. Then, even if he answered instantaneously, it took another 1.3 seconds for his response carried by radio waves to come back, for a total roundtrip time of 2.6 seconds or about 3 seconds, if he paused a little bit to think.

The delay that we heard when listening in the late1960s and early 1970s to the astronauts on the Moon is due simply to the time it takes for light to travel between the Moon, and us and between the Moon and us. There you can actually see a practical application. In fact, if you make a long distance phone call to the other side of the world, you can actually hear a little bit of a delay sometimes when you're talking with another person because the light is actually bouncing from one station to another. It actually goes some reasonable fraction of a second in time between you and your friend.

The point of all this is that light travel time is proportional to distance. If we say that time is distance over speed, then it's one over the speed, times the distance. Since the speed of light is constant and doesn't change, at least not in a vacuum, this is a constant of proportionality. The only thing that is changing for different objects is the distance from us; the speed of light is the same.

For example, if I travel from my home in Oakland to the Sierra Nevada Mountains, that's a distance of 180 miles. If I travel at 60 miles an hour, it takes me three hours to traverse that distance. If I instead want to go to Los Angeles, which is about 360 miles away, then it takes me six hours because Los Angeles, at 360 miles, is twice as far away as the mountains are, and it takes me twice as long to traverse that distance traveling at the same speed.

Using an astronomical example, we can determine the time it takes for light to travel from the Sun. The Sun, you might know, is 390 times farther than the Moon. Now, you might not know that. It's probably easier to remember the distance of the Moon and the Sun, which is 93 million miles, for the case of the Sun. You could have plugged in those numbers into distance equals speed times time, but I'm saying suppose you knew how much farther away the Sun is than the Moon. It's 390 times farther. Then, knowing the amount of time it took for light to travel from the Moon to us—1.3 seconds— it's easy to calculate the amount of time it took to travel from the Sun to us. That would simply be 390 times longer because the Sun is 390 times farther away than the Moon.

Looking at the slide, 390 x 1.3 is 500 seconds or, converting to minutes, the Sun is 8.3 light minutes away. A light minute is just like a regular minute, but less filling. You can think of it that way. The Sun's light took 8.3 minutes to reach us, so we are seeing it as it was 8.3 minutes in the past. I did this calculation using these proportionalities, not because in this particular case it was easier to do so, but because later in the course there will be instances where it's much easier to think of proportionalities, and things relative to each other, than it is to actually plug all the numbers and all the gory details into the equations.

We're looking at the Sun and we see it as it was 8.3 minutes ago. What that means is that someone, or something, could have turned out or turned off the Sun, and we wouldn't know it for about 8.3 minutes because the light that it emitted has already been on its way. We would continue to see that light for 8.3 minutes, and then the Sun will blink out and we can all express cries of agony.

A light year is the distance light travels in one year. This is where things start getting more interesting. Distance is speed times time, the speed is 360 kilometers per second, and the time is one year. You can't just multiply these two numbers simply because the units don't cancel out. You first have to convert one year into seconds, in order to make sure that everything balances out. That is not so hard to do. One year equals 365.25 days; a day is 24 hours, 24 hours a day. So, you see the days will cancel out. An hour is 60 minutes, so the hours will cancel out. A minute is 60 seconds and so you see the minutes will cancel out. If I multiplied distance equals speed times time and converted one year into seconds, we would find that the units of distance (kilometers per second) cancel out with the units of time (seconds), leaving just the unit of distance (kilometers). The distance that light travels at its finite speed in one year is 9.5 trillion kilometers, about 6 trillion miles. That is an immense distance. Try traveling it in your automobile at 60 miles per hour. It will take you a very long time.

It is this sort of distance that will become very useful to us as we explore the distances of stars and other galaxies, objects very far away. We don't want to carry around numbers like 10 trillion kilometers or 10 quadrillion kilometers. We want to express the numbers in ways that are smaller and ways that are easily digestible. This light year distance, the distance light travels in a year, is a very convenient unit of measure.

Here in this slide, we see Alpha Centauri at the left. That is the nearest star. Actually, it's a star system—a couple of stars. The companion of the bright one that you see here is actually a little bit closer than the bright star itself. The companion is called Proxima Centauri and is 4.3 light years away, so the nearest star is 4.3 light years away. It has taken a little over four years for that light to reach us.

Other stars that you see are typically tens, hundreds or even thousands of light years away. You can begin to see now why astronomers like this unit. The initial examples of the distances of people or the Moon may have sounded silly, but we lead up to distances that are immense. Most stars in our galaxy are many light years away—thousands of light years, even tens of thousands of light years. Our galaxy is 100,000 light years across. If you were at one end of our galaxy and you wanted to send a message to a friend at the other end, it would take 100,000 years for your message to reach that friend. "Hello, let's go get a pizza." It would then take 100,000 years for the reply to come back. Suppose your friend said, "Yeah, let's have some beer along with it." That fragment of a conversation would have taken 200,000 years to transpire. Hardly a stimulating conversation, but I'm sorry, that is just the way the Universe is; it's immense.

If we look at this slide, we see the nearest big galaxy to our own. This is the Andromeda Galaxy. It is a collection of hundreds of billions of stars, much like our Sun. It is a little over two million light years away and it's the nearest big galaxy. So, we are seeing the light from the stars in that galaxy as it was 2 million years ago. It was emitted long before the first *Homo sapiens* were on Earth and about the time when the first hominids were wandering around—*Australopithecus* and things like that.

If they, by the same token, are looking at us right now, they will not see us as we are right now, but rather they will see our ancestors. They will see the Earth as it was two million years ago, if they are looking at us right now. To view this lecture, we have to fast forward their clocks by two million years and then they could view this lecture, if we were to send it to them.

In this slide, you see galaxies that are much farther away. Almost all of the dots in this picture are galaxies—like our Milky Way and the Andromeda Galaxy, full of hundreds of billions of stars—but they look so small because they themselves are billions of light years away. Not just two million, like the Andromeda Galaxy, but billions of light years away. We see them, as they were billions of years ago.

You can see now that the finite speed of light gives us the opportunity to see a movie of the past history of the Universe. By looking towards progressively greater distances, we see the Universe as it was in progressively greater times in the past. If we assume that we are in a typical part of the Universe, and other parts of the Universe that we observe are also typical—we have got to test those assumptions, of course—we can say, "That's sort of what we used to look like billions of years ago."

For example, looking at these four galaxies that are about four or five billion light years away, they look kind of scraggily and misshapen. They don't look quite as majestic and well formed as the spiral galaxy Andromeda or our spiral galaxy. We can try to see whether, theoretically, we can understand whether galaxies should have, or should not have, looked that way in the past. The point is that whatever our theories say, we can compare them with direct observations of what galaxies used to look like. It is the finite speed of light that allows us to do this. If light were instantaneously fast, we would not have the opportunity to do this.

Here are four quasars. They look like stars and, for a long time, people thought that they were just peculiar stars. But they turn out to be the hearts of galaxies many billions of light years away, when voracious black holes were probably eating huge amounts of material in the centers of these galaxies. Quasars do not exist now, but we see them at very large distances. Therefore, they are the denizens of the Universe as it was in the past. They no longer exist. It is as though they are the dinosaurs. The quasars are now extinct. We see them at great distances, not here; hence, we see them far back in the past, not now.

Astronomers also need to consider matter on very small scales. I've considered the very large; now let me look at the very small. Here is an atom. An atom, as I will discuss later, consists of a very small nucleus, which has protons and neutrons in it, and then a cloud of electrons surrounding it. The proton is 10^{-15} meters in size. I wouldn't express that in light years, because that would be really silly. A proton is 10^{-15} meters in size or 10^{-13} centimeters; it's tiny. The electron cloud around it is about 50,000 times bigger, so, the electron cloud around it is perhaps 5×10^{-11} meters. It varies between 10^{-10} and 10^{-11}. I chose a number in between, but it's roughly 10,000-100,000 bigger than the nucleus.

In between, there is nothing. We think that between the electron cloud and the nucleus of an atom, there is essentially empty space. If you think about the volume of a sphere, it's the cube, or the third power, of the radius. If the electron cloud is 10[000]-100,000 times as big as the nucleus, this means that the volume of an atom is 10^{12} to 10^{15} times the volume of the nucleus. It's immensely bigger than the nucleus, and most of that volume is empty space.

We are made of atoms, little tiny nuclei surrounded by clouds of electrons. Most of that space is empty, so all of us are mostly empty space. We're 99.9999999999 percent empty space. When I first learned that, I was blown away. In fact, I didn't believe it, but there are experiments that show that nuclei really are so small and that the clouds of electrons are considerably bigger. Still very small compared to anything that we can see, but much bigger.

To put this into perspective, it's useful to consider scale models. Here is the Sun, for example. Let's suppose that the Sun is the size of the period at the end of a sentence. The Sun is about 1.5 million kilometers in diameter or 110 times the diameter of the Earth. It's a big thing. Let's suppose that these 1.5 million kilometers, 100 times the size of the Earth, is the size of a period at the end of the sentence, which is about 0.5 millimeter in size. This will be a scale model.

Using this scale model, how close would the nearest star be? It turns out it would be about 13 or 14 kilometers away. A star five light years away would be about 16 kilometers away. Proxima Centauri, the very nearest star, would be 13 or 14 kilometers away. Typical stars would be many tens or hundreds of kilometers away, even thousands of kilometers away, on a scale where the Sun is the size of a period. All of that space is pretty empty. There's some gas and dust, but mostly it's empty space. In between, this little dot the size of a period and the nearest stars are some tens of kilometers of empty space. It kind of resembles an atom, in terms of its emptiness.

The Milky Way Galaxy, which is about 100,000 light years in diameter, would be about 320,000 kilometers in diameter. That's nearly the distance between Earth and the Moon. If you shrunk the Sun to the size of a period, our galaxy would span the distance nearly to that of the Moon. That gives you an idea of the immensity of our galaxy compared to the size of our Sun, which is, itself, very large compared to the Earth—110 times as large. The Earth is immense, compared with us, and we're immense compared with atoms. So, you see the enormous range of scales that we are discussing in the Universe.

Now let's suppose, instead, that an atom is the size of an apple, about 8 centimeters in diameter. We're going to blow an atom up to this size. A human is 20 billion times bigger in length than an atom; we're about 20 billion atoms across in a sense. If you multiply 8 centimeters, the size of this apple, by 20 billion, you get 1.6 million kilometers. So, a human would be 1.6 million kilometers in length if an atom were the size of an apple. 1.6 million kilometers is about four times the distance to the Moon. We would be quite gargantuan compared to an atom the size of this apple.

That gives you some idea of how small the constituent particles of which we are made really are. They are tiny. If the atom were the size of an apple, how big would the nucleus of the atom be? It turns out it would be roughly 1/1,000,000 of a meter, one micrometer. On the scale of this apple, which represents the size of the electron cloud, the nucleus buried within that atom is 1/1,000,000 of a meter in size, not discernible by our eyes.

The atom is mostly empty space and goes down to very small numbers: 10^{-15} meters for the size of a proton, even smaller for subatomic particles. At the other end of the scale, we are talking about billions of light years, the distances to which astronomers can see galaxies. That range of distances, and the fact that humans are actually roughly in the middle of that range, is a very interesting sobering aspect of the Universe.

We will later consider what the Universe would have been like if some of the constants of nature were different, or if some of the laws of physics were a little bit different from what they are. It turns out many of these distances and things would end up being very different. Many of the physical processes that had to have occurred in order for life to develop wouldn't have occurred because, in fact, if you change a few little things around, it just doesn't work out right.

Somehow, the Universe spans this large scale of distances and has the properties that it does, and we are here pondering these questions. If it were a little different, it would have looked very different from what we actually now see. If the laws of physics were such that atoms were not as small as they are, and galaxies were not as big as they are, then you can show that life, at least as we know it, probably wouldn't have developed. Studies of objects at many different distances give us some idea of the total range of phenomena that we are exploring and give us some insight in how it is that sentient beings could have formed.

Lecture Three
Light—The Supreme Informant

Scope:

Astronomers obtain most of their information through the analysis of light. This lecture introduces the technique of spectroscopy, where light is dispersed into its component colors, as in a rainbow. We find that light consists of electromagnetic waves: oscillating electric and magnetic fields. The complete electromagnetic spectrum spans a vast range of wavelengths—from gamma rays to radio waves—but our eyes are sensitive to only a tiny fraction. Light can also behave as discrete particles called photons; each photon has an energy that is inversely proportional to its wavelength. A given experiment can be used to measure either the wave-like or particle-like properties of light, but not both simultaneously. The strange wave/particle duality of light is a fundamental aspect of quantum theory. Actually, we now know that this duality extends to normal matter as well: all particles have wave-like properties.

Objectives

Upon completion of this lecture, you should be able to:

1. Explain what is meant by the spectrum of an object.
2. Describe the wave nature of light and the properties of the wave.
3. Define the wavelength, frequency, period, and speed of a wave. State the relationships between these variables.
4. Discuss the different types of electromagnetic radiation, and their order from longest to shortest wavelength, including visible light.
5. State the relationship between the energy and frequency (or wavelength) of a photon.
6. Summarize some arguments for thinking that light has both wave-like and particle-like properties.

Outline

I. Analysis of light is by far the primary method with which astronomers obtain information about the Universe.

    A. In this way, astronomy differs from much of physics, chemistry, geology, and biology. It is an *observational* science; classical *experiments* generally can't be done. A physicist, for example, can weigh an object to measure its mass, submerge it in water to find its volume, and break it open to see what's inside.

B. There are a few counterexamples.
1. Meteorites are found on Earth.
2. Probes are sent to planets and moons.
3. Energetic particles reach us from great distances.

C. An object in the sky can be *photographed*, revealing its brightness, shape, and relative position.
1. The stars in a cluster, for example, have different brightness.
2. Photographs obtained through different filters can be appropriately combined to give a nearly "true color" rendition.

D. The *spectrum* of the object can also be analyzed.
1. If one passes "white light" (ordinary sunlight) through a glass prism or water droplets, a rainbow (spectrum) is formed.
2. The fictitious character "Roy G. Biv" serves as a good mnemonic for the order of the colors of the rainbow (although the color "indigo" is now rarely used).
3. The brightness (intensity) of light coming from a given object can be plotted as a function of color after passing the light through a prism, for quantitative analysis of the object's spectrum.

II. Visible light is one type of electromagnetic radiation or electromagnetic wave.

A. The waves consist of self-propagating, oscillating electric and magnetic fields that are perpendicular to each other and perpendicular to the direction of motion.
1. A static electric field exists around a stationary charge such as an electron.
2. A static magnetic field exists around a stationary magnet.
3. There is a deep connection between electric and magnetic fields. For example, a current (which consists of electrons in motion through a wire) produces a magnetic field, as in an electromagnet. Conversely,

passing a loop of wire through a magnetic field produces a current in the wire.

4. Sustained rotation of the magnet or back-and-forth motion of the charge produces a continuous disturbance in the associated field: the strength and direction of the field oscillate (change sinusoidally) with time.

5. An oscillating electric field produces an oscillating magnetic field, and vice versa. These propagate outward as electromagnetic waves. The phenomenon is fully described by James Clerk Maxwell's four equations of electromagnetism.

6. The *wavelength*, denoted by the Greek letter λ (lambda), is the distance from one wave crest to the next. This has the units of length, such as cm.

7. The *frequency*, denoted by the Greek letter ν (nu), is the number of times per second that a crest passes a fixed point Q; the units are 1/seconds, or Hertz (Hz). Hence, the *period* of the wave, P (in seconds), is simply $1/\nu$.

8. In general, the length per wave (λ) multiplied by the number of waves per second (ν) gives the length per second traversed by the wave. This is its *speed* v: $\lambda\nu = v$. In our case, $v = c$, the speed of light.

B. Different colors of visible light correspond to electromagnetic waves having different wavelengths.

1. The typical unit of wavelength measurement of visible light is the Angstrom (Å), which is 10^{-10} meters or 0.1 nanometer (0.1 nm).

2. Violet, blue, green, yellow, orange, and red light correspond to wavelengths of about 4000 Å, 4500 Å, 5000 Å, 5500 Å, 6000 Å, and 6500 Å, respectively.

III. The complete electromagnetic spectrum spans a vast range of wavelengths.

A. The main types are as follows, but the numerical dividing lines are only approximate.

1. Gamma rays have wavelengths shorter than about 0.1 Å.

2. X-rays have wavelengths roughly in the range 0.1 to 100 Å.

3. Ultraviolet (UV) light spans wavelengths of 100 to 4000 Å.

    4. Visible (optical) light is in the range 4000 to 7000 Å.

    5. Infrared (IR) radiation goes from 7000 Å to about 1 mm.

    6. Radio waves are longer than 1 mm, and often up to 10 km or more.

B. There are no *qualitative* differences between the types, but the instruments and techniques used to detect them are often very different.

C. The human eye is sensitive to visible light (4000 to 7000 Å), only a minuscule fraction of the entire electromagnetic spectrum.

D. All electromagnetic waves in a *vacuum* travel with the *same* speed, c, regardless of λ. The measured speed of light is *independent* of the relative speeds of the observer and the light source. This is admittedly counterintuitive, but it has been completely verified; indeed, it is one of the foundations of Einstein's theory of relativity.

E. Electromagnetic waves slow down in media such as glass and water, and the speed is generally a function of wavelength. This, in fact, is what leads to the dispersion (spreading out) of the colors when light passes through a prism.

IV. Light can also behave as discrete particles known as *photons* (wave or energy "packets"). This is a fundamental aspect of quantum theory.

    A. One of the most important phenomena demonstrating this is known as the "Compton effect."

        1. Electromagnetic radiation of wavelength λ_0 striking a stationary electron scatters off with a longer wavelength, $\lambda > \lambda_0$. This cannot be explained in the wave model.

        2. The shift in wavelength is easily understood if a photon hit the electron, giving it some energy of motion and thereby losing some of its own energy.

    B. With the right equipment, photons can be detected as discrete lumps of energy.

        1. A photon has no rest mass, but its energy E is given by the product of Planck's constant h (named after the quantum physicist Max Planck) and its frequency v: $E = h\nu$. Planck's constant is very small: 6.627×10^{-27} erg seconds, where an erg is a unit of energy.

2. Photons of higher energy therefore have higher frequency and shorter wavelength: $E = h\nu = hc/\lambda$, since $\lambda\nu = c$.

3. The photon nature of light is most easily recognized at high energies: objects generally emit gamma rays and X-rays so rarely that the photons are detected one at a time.

C. Collectively, many photons having the same energy produce an electromagnetic wave with the corresponding wavelength λ. Sunlight and the light from most bulbs consist of photons having a broad range of energies or wavelengths.

D. Each *individual* photon has wave-like properties, too.

1. Constructive and destructive interference effects, such as those seen in waves flowing through gaps in a breakwater, are produced even when photons are sent *one at a time* through holes in a screen.

2. A photon must therefore interfere with itself, and it can only do this by passing through all of the holes; it behaves like a wave!

3. If the experiment is modified in such as was as to actually *determine* which hole the photon went through, the interference (wave-like) effects disappear. The photon acts like a particle in this case; the measurement "disturbs" the photon, destroying the wave.

4. Thus, either the wave-like or particle-like properties of light can be measured in a given experiment; both cannot be measured simultaneously.

E. It turns out that the wave/particle duality of light is also a quantum aspect of normal matter.

1. An electron, for example, can behave as a wave of wavelength $\lambda = h/mv$, where m is its mass and v is its speed relative to the observer. Electrons passing through holes in a screen produce interference effects, just as light does.

2. The large masses of most particles imply that their wavelengths are exceedingly small, making it more difficult to discern their wave-like nature than is the case for light.

Essential Reading:

Gribbin, J. *In Search of Schrodinger's Cat: Quantum Physics and Reality*. Bantam, 1984.

Pagels, H. *The Cosmic Code: Quantum Physics as the Language of Nature*. Simon and Schuster, 1982.

Sobel, M. *Light*. Univ. Chicago Press, 1987.

Verschuur, G.L. *Hidden Attraction: The History and Mystery of Magnetism*. Oxford Univ. Press, 1993.

Wolf, F. A. *Taking the Quantum Leap: The New Physics for Nonscientists*. Perennial Library, 1989.

Questions to Consider:

1. How can it be possible for something to have both wave-like and particle-like properties?

2. What are some examples in which you know that magnetic or electric fields play a prominent role? Is there evidence that one type of field induces or interacts with the other?

Lecture Three—Transcript
Light—The Supreme Informant

Astronomers, unlike other scientists, get almost all of their information from the light that they gather from the Universe. Physicists, chemists, biologists and geologists can actually do experiments in laboratories. A physicist, for example, can take a rock and weigh it and convert that weight to a mass and submerge it in water to figure out its volume (The amount by which the water rises in the beaker tells the volume of the rock.). A geologist can break it open and see what's inside and maybe put some acid on it and see how it reacts with the rock.

But an astronomer, with some very few exceptions, cannot do that. We can't go out and grab the stars and, if we could, we would burn our hands. We have a few exceptions in the form of meteorites, for example, shown in this slide, where the rocks come down from the skies to us and we can do the sorts of things that I just said. Or in some cases, astronauts have gone to the moon and brought back rocks to us or we've sent probes to some of the planets. A probe was sent into the atmosphere of Jupiter to see what its composition was. We also get some charged particles from outer space called cosmic rays, and we can analyze their composition.

With few such exceptions, the only real handle we have on the Universe is through light. Light is the one thing that we need to analyze as thoroughly as we possibly can, in order to obtain as many clues to the nature of the Universe as possible from this one thing that we get.

There are a number of ways of using light to study the Universe. If you look at a picture of stars, for example, you see that they have different levels of brightness. Here is a star that's way brighter than another star. You can measure the special position of stars relative to each other and come to some conclusions about the distribution of matter in the Universe. You can also take pictures through different filters—say, a blue filter and a yellow filter and a red filter—and come up with some sort of a relatively true color of the object, if you're careful in how you combine the light from those filters.

Here is a slide of a nebula, a glowing cloud of gas and dust where the colors that you see are reasonably true to what the object would look like if you had very sensitive eyes. We will discuss later what produces the color, but the reds are produced by glowing hydrogen atoms and the blues are produced by atoms and particles reflecting light. Reflection tends to accentuate the blues. Sometimes you can get nice true color pictures of astronomical objects and study their radiation in that way.

I should add that many of the astronomical photographs that you see are false color renditions of what is really out there. The false colors are adjusted to correspond with the intensity of light. For example: bright might be green and dim might be purple or something like that. The objects aren't really all these fantastic colors. We, with our feeble eyes, generally don't see colors very well when the light is weak because our eyes are straining to see the light at all, and they just can't see the colors.

An extremely useful technique in astronomy, besides taking pictures of objects, is to pass the light through a prism or a raindrop. Nature does this in the form of rainbows for us, where white light— sunlight—is passing through little droplets of water, and those droplets of water are bending the light—refracting it—into particular angles for particular colors. We see from the rainbow effect that white light consists of a multitude of colors.

We can't reproduce in the laboratory a rainbow very well with droplets of water, but we can use a prism. If you pass light through a little triangular piece of glass like this, as indicated in the image, that glass disperses or breaks the white light into its component colors in exactly the same way that water does. The details are different actually in how many reflections and refractions there are, but the principle is the same.

If you look then at these colors, you see the classic rainbow going from violet to red or red to violet. An easy way to remember the colors is just to recall the friendly fellow Roy G. Biv: Red, Orange, Yellow, Green, Blue, Indigo, Violet. Indigo is between blue and violet. It is sort of an obsolete color, but Newton thought it up because he wanted there to be seven colors corresponding to seven notes and various harmonics and things like that. But you rarely hear about the color indigo anymore. Anyway, Roy G. Biv gives us the colors of the spectrum, or the colors of the rainbow.

If you then go and you use an instrument to measure the quantity of light at every different wave length from blue to red and measure the amount of radiation, the amount of energy, at each of those colors and plot the distribution of that brightness—or intensity or amount of energy—along a vertical axis and the color along a horizontal axis, you get what's called a spectrum.

Here we show brightness along the vertical axis, color along the horizontal axis going from violet to red. Then that distribution that a particular object gives out is called a spectrum of that object. The act of getting a spectrum is called spectroscopy. Spectroscopy is one of the most powerful techniques that we use in astronomy. Much of what I tell you during these forty lectures will be based on the spectroscopic analysis of light.

It is true that the pictures are very useful as well. The pictures from, say, the Hubble Space Telescope are normally what you see in newspapers and on TV shows, but it is fair to say that even more information about the physical characteristics of matter, stars and galaxies has been obtained through their spectra than through their images. So spectroscopy is very important but doesn't produce as pretty a picture, and that's why we rarely see it in the newspapers.

What is this quantity then? What is this substance that we call light? It behooves us to understand light if it's so important to the process of understanding the Universe. What is light? I'd like to devote this whole lecture to what light is; it's that important a subject.

It turns out that light is an electromagnetic wave. It is a wave of electric and magnetic fields that are oscillating around—in strength and direction—and are profligating in a direction perpendicular to the direction in which they are oscillating. I'll define all this now in the next few minutes, but it's basically an electromagnetic wave. The different colors that you see are different wave lengths, or frequencies, of that electromagnetic wave.

Let me discuss then electricity and magnetism for a few minutes. If we look at this slide here, we see that there are a bunch of radial rods coming out of a sphere. This is what we think the electric field of, for example, a proton or an electron, looks like. It's, basically, radially directed lines which indicate that if you were to place another positive charge next to that proton at rest and then release it, that second proton would be radially propelled away from the first one. Similarly, an electron, which has the opposite charge of a proton, would be radially attracted toward the proton. You could have a single charge just sitting out there and the lines of force would just stream outwards like this, and they can be essentially never ending. In principle, you could have only one charge in the whole Universe. That's not what it is made of, but you could have just one lone electric charge sitting there.

A magnetic field is quite different. Here we see a bar magnet kind of like the one that I have right here. A bar magnet has a north and a South Pole. The magnetic force, the magnetic field lines, loops from one end to the other. You can see that in the picture. The arrow goes from the North Pole and loops down in to the South Pole.

I have a little demo here that shows that as well. There is a solution, which has a whole bunch of little tiny pieces of iron in it, and a magnet down inside the solution. You can see how the little iron filings align themselves in a fuzzy way with these lines of force. The iron filings align themselves to follow the curvatures of these lines of force. This looks very different from what we saw when we considered an electric field.

Another difference, which you can see here, is that if you break a bar magnet in half, each of those pieces behaves like the original in that the lines of force start at the North Pole, loop around and come down to a South Pole. So a bar magnet always has a North Pole and a South Pole. Any magnet always has a North Pole and a South Pole. The lines loop around and come back to the object that omits them. That's quite unlike the electric charge, where the lines of force went out radially, effectively to infinity, if you let them do that. Bar magnets and other magnets do not do that.

So magnetic and electric fields seem different. For a long time, they were thought to be quite different beasts, but clearly there is a very deep connection between electric and magnetic fields. Let me illustrate that with a little demonstration here.

If I have a nail and I wrap a wire around it, but I don't connect the other end of the wire to the battery, the nail, not being magnetic, does not pick up these other smaller nails. But now if I connect the wire to the battery and send a current through it, you will see that the big nail easily picks up all the small ones. When I disconnect the system, they drop down.

A current produces a magnetic field. A current is just a bunch of little charges moving along and they produce a magnetic field. What a wonderful discovery. If we have another magnet, and we repel the end of this first one here, you can see that if you do this in the right way, you can actually make a motor. The way motors are made is that actually first the North Pole is repelled and then the South Pole, then the North Pole, then the South Pole, the North Pole, the South Pole and so on. You can see that if you have an alternating current, where the poles switch around back and forth, and that alternating current is timed in precisely the right way, you can make an object rotate, and that is the basis on which motors operate.

There is this deep connection between electric and magnetic fields illustrated by the currents. There's an even deeper connection. If you rotate this bar magnet, or the magnet that is rotating over there, it turns out that you are changing the configuration of the magnetic field that surrounds it. Clearly, you're rotating it so that all of these field lines are going around in some funny way and that produces an electric field. Experimentally, that's what we've found.

Similarly, if you take a charge and oscillate it up and down, then what you're doing is producing a kink in those radial field lines, and that kink propagates along and actually generates a magnetic field. So, changes in an electric field produce a magnetic field, and changes in a magnetic field produce an electric field. If you can get one of these guys going—suppose you rotate a magnet and produce a changing magnetic field—that will, itself, produce a changing electric field. But the changes in the electric field will produce changes in the magnetic field, which then will lead to changes in the electric field, and so on.

You can see, in fact, what you're doing: you're producing an oscillation in the magnetic and electric fields and that is what light is. It is oscillating electric and magnetic fields, which, once started, once you emit your flashlight beam, will continue almost like a perpetual motion machine, unless they are blocked by some sort of a substance or a telescope, or something like that. They will continue through a vacuum unaided by any force from the outside world, because once you've started those electric fields changing, they will produce magnetic fields which change, and so on and so forth. The light propagates itself outwards through space.

So that is what light is. Let me illustrate that then in this diagram. I'm plotting along one axis a bunch of arrows, which change height. Let's call that the magnetic field. Then they change direction. They go bigger, then smaller. Then they change direction. They go bigger and smaller, and so on. That changing magnetic field, which I could have produced by rotating my magnet, induces an electric field, which also changes in size and direction. It's perpendicular to the magnetic field. If the magnetic field is oscillating up and down in this direction, then the electric field will oscillate back and forth in a perpendicular direction.

Both of those directions are perpendicular to the direction in which this whole pattern will propagate. That is the direction in which the light travels. In this diagram, that is the direction towards the right of the picture.

That is an electromagnetic wave, and visible light is one form of this electromagnetic wave, or electromagnetic radiation. That's what light is.

In 1864, a fellow named Maxwell realized all this and put it all together in the form of four equations which can fit on a tee shirt. These are the equations of electricity and magnetism. Although three of the four had been deduced by people before Maxwell, he added a crucial component to the fourth equation and also brought them all together, manipulated them and realized that what they described when properly manipulated was the propagation of a wave of electric and magnetic fields, with a speed that coincidentally happened to be the speed of light. So, he came to the realization that electric and magnetic fields produce light in this way.

Let's now define some terms in our discussion of these waves. We can define the wavelength to be the distance between two consecutive crests of a wave or between two consecutive troughs if you want. Any two consecutive corresponding points of the wave can be used to define the wavelength. That's measured in, say, meters; it's a length. It's been noted by the Greek symbol λ (lambda).

Greek ν (nu) is the frequency and that's the number of times per second that a crest passes by a given point; call it Q. So you just stand there as point Q, and you measure how many times per second a wave crest goes past you, and that would be the frequency of the wave. Suppose 10 wave crests go past you per second. The frequency of the wave would be 10 per second, or 10 hertz. A hertz is a unit of per second.

If 100 wave crests go by per second, the frequency would be 100 hertz. Notice, of course, that the frequency and the period of a wave must be related. The inverse of the frequency is the period of a wave. If 50 crests went by per second, they clearly, each of them, occupy only 1/50 of a second. So the period is 1/50 of a second, the inverse of the frequency.

You can also see that the length per wave, the wavelength (λ), multiplied by the number of waves that go by per second (v) is simply the length per second of this wave that goes past you. That's the speed of the wave (v). The length per second is the speed. This is in fact a general relationship; the wavelength times the frequency is the speed of the wave.

$$\lambda v = v$$

In this case, since we're describing light, that speed is c, the speed of light (300,000 kilometers per second, 186,000 miles per second).

Light, as I just mentioned, is only one form of electromagnetic radiation, but it's the form that we can see. It's the form that corresponds to the different colors of the rainbow. If you give the wavelength in nanometers—which are billionths of a meter as shown here, or in angstroms, which are ten-billionths of a meter (a nanometer is just 10 angstroms) —then red light corresponds to a wave having 6,500 of these angstrom units, or 650 nanometers.

What does that mean? That means that when I look at a red shirt, the light that I'm seeing has a wavelength of only 650 billionths of a meter, because a nanometer is a billionth of a meter. You cannot actually discern the wavelength of light directly, but it manifests itself indirectly in the form of different colors. Yellow has a wavelength of 550 nanometers. Green has a wavelength of about 500 nanometers or 5,000 angstroms. I will use both types of units in this course. Blue has a wavelength of 4,500 angstroms or 450 nanometers.

They have different lengths, and none of these lengths can we directly measure by using a ruler or anything like that, because they're miniscule. But our eyes are clearly sensitive to these different wavelengths because they perceive them to be different colors. Our eyes are not omnipotent. They don't see all possible wavelengths. In fact, as shown here, we see that our eyes are sensitive to only a tiny fraction of the entire electromagnetic spectrum. It doesn't look very large on this television screen, but it's enormous. This television screen has the graph in what's called logarithmic units. We show ten kilometers here, and every tick mark corresponds to a reduction in length by a factor of ten. So, one kilometer, 0.1, and so forth, all the way down to the right-hand side, where we're talking about lengths that are small fractions of a billionth of a meter. So we're going from a billionth of a meter on the right-hand side to ten kilometers, or even more, on the left-hand side. That is the entire electromagnetic spectrum. In fact, it actually extends beyond ten kilometers and even less than a hundredth of a billionth of a meter. I just don't want to show all possibilities here because, in fact, the graph would be infinitely long and you wouldn't see any part of it on the television screen.

The visible light is just a tiny fraction. It is a fraction that goes from 400 nanometers up to 700 nanometers, not even a factor of ten in wavelength and almost nothing compared with the many factors of ten shown in this diagram.

Our eyes are sensitive only to a small fraction of what's out there, but astronomers would like to study all that's out there because different types of objects emit preferentially different forms of electromagnetic radiation, depending on what they are doing. We will see, for example, that hot objects tend to omit bluer light than cold objects. Exploding stars might emit very short-wave radiation right when they are exploding. Little electrons swaying through the weak magnetic field of our galaxy might emit very long waves, things like radio waves. Radio waves have lengths of meters or tens of meters. Infrared radiation is just somewhat longer than visible light. Ultraviolet is somewhat shorter; X rays are even shorter, and gamma rays are shorter still.

All these different types of electromagnetic radiation produce different types of astronomical objects. We would like to study those objects in the form of these different forms of electromagnetic radiation, in order to deduce as much as we can about their physical properties.

There are no qualitative differences between these different types of radiation. All of them are electromagnetic fields that are produced by oscillating electric and magnetic fields self-supporting each other. But there are very many different detection techniques for these waves. You detect optical photons with eyes or photographic film.

You can detect gamma rays with light-sensitive crystals and things like that. You can detect ultraviolet radiation in different ways. The detection techniques are very different although qualitatively all these things are the same sort of substance.

All of them travel with the same speed through a vacuum, and that is the speed of light (300,000 kilometers per second). That speed is independent of the wavelength that you are studying.

In glass or water, waves can slow down. The speed of light is not the highest possible speed in glass or water, light can actually slow down. It only travels at 300,000 kilometers per second in a vacuum. It can slow down in certain substances. It is interesting, but the reason that a prism disperses light into its different colors is because the light that's blue is traveling with a different speed than the light that's red. If you look at the little waves that are going through microscopically, the slower speed of the blue waves makes them actually bend more in the prism than is the case for the red waves. That's an interesting aspect of waves.

The other interesting thing is that certain particles can actually travel faster than the speed of light in a medium where the speed of light is depressed. For example, if you're sending light through water, the speed of light is actually two thirds or so of what it is in a vacuum. You can actually send particles through that water faster than the local speed of light, as long as you do not exceed the global speed of light, which is the basis of all of relativity, light is the fastest possible speed and it cannot be exceeded. But in certain circumstances, the depressed speed of light can be exceeded, and we will actually make use of that later on when we study the detection of exploding stars.

Another interesting thing about light, which is also one of the foundations of relativity, is that the measured speed of light is independent of the frame of reference from which you are viewing it. For example, if I am at rest and you shine a flashlight beam at me, I will measure its speed to be 300,000 kilometers per second. But if you now shine a beam at me and I'm running toward you at the speed of light—I'm Superman let's say—I will still measure that light to have a speed of 300,000 kilometers per second. It is independent of my speed.

It is also independent of your speed. If you're coming toward me relative to the laboratory at some speed, I will still measure the speed of light to be 300,000 kilometers per second. That's the basis of relativity, and there is a very interesting course on that topic produced by The Teaching Company, which I urge you to view.

We can tell that light is a wave because it behaves in a way that is similar to that of phenomena that are clearly wavelike. Here we have a water tank with two pins that are tapping the surface of the water. The tapping motion produces crests and troughs, crests and troughs and so on, emerging from each of these two centers where the tapping is occurring.

You can see that the pattern is such that in some places, the wave crests constructively interfere with each other and produce a higher wave. In other places, the crests and troughs interfere with each other destructively to produce essentially no undulation of the water at that particular position in that moment in time.

We've got regions here in which there are troughs and regions, here where there is constructive interference, and we have high waves—high up waves and high down waves. This sort of constructive and destructive interference is a very characteristic property of waves. You can see this when you look, for example, at the waves hitting a breakwater. If they move through holes in the breakwater, you will see them emerging at little circular wavelengths beyond those holes, and then they will constructively and destructively interfere to produce a pattern of this sort.

When light does this, we see the same sort of thing. Incident light hitting two little holes produces circular wavelets, which propagate outwards from each of the two holes. Where the crests meet each other, such as at this position, you get a reinforcement of the amplitude of the wave—here and here and here—but at intermediate locations, such as where the arrow is pointing right now, one wave pressed from the right-hand opening is coincident with a trough from the left-hand opening, and you get a destructive interference of the light.

If you're just seeing this diagram, you might say, "Well, I'm just telling you on faith that this is what light does." But that's not really true. Here is an actual picture of the pattern that is formed when light is allowed to pass through two holes like this. There are, indeed, regions where the light constructively interferes and other regions between where it destructively interferes, where there is essentially no light.

This sort of pattern of bright-dark-bright-dark-bright-dark that we see in light is exactly the kind of pattern that we would see if we were to cut a plane through the water emerging from two holes in a breakwater. We would see regions where the amplitude of the waves is very high and regions where there are essentially no waves or motion of the water. You have this constructive and destructive interference in water and you have it in light as well. This is conclusive proof that light is clearly a wave, verifying ideas that Maxwell had in 1864, that it is some sort of an oscillation of electric fields and magnetic fields in a wave-like way.

If that were the full story, light would be somewhat boring. It's not the full story. Light also behaves as a particle. This was shown in a number of ways early in the 20th century. It was quite unexpected. Perhaps the easiest way to see it is in one of the subsequent experiments that were done in 1923. It is known as the Compton effect.

If you have an electron sitting at rest in your laboratory, and an electromagnetic wave comes along with a certain wavelength that you measure to be λ_0—call it "lambda naught, the original wavelength of the wave—then what would happen classically if light were only a wave, is that it would oscillate with charge back and forth. Light has an electric field, and it would interact with the electron. It would push on it back and forth as the electric field changes direction and amplitude.

That electron then would oscillate back and forth with exactly the same frequency as the incident wave, because that is what's pushing on it back and forth, back and forth like this, with the frequency of the wave. It should then emit a wave; it should effectively scatter the light, at the same frequency, at the same wavelength, because as it's jostling back and forth, and because the electric field is pulling on it, the electron itself would emit waves of exactly the same wavelength. You would expect the scattered light from the electron to have exactly the same wavelength as the incident light (phonetic).

What, in fact, is observed? What's observed is that the scattered light has a wavelength longer than the incident light. λ of this new wave is bigger than λ_0. It's a longer wave. It's a lower frequency because the longer the wavelength, the lower the frequency. Moreover, the speed of the electron is no longer zero. It's no longer at rest in the laboratory. It's actually moving a little bit through the laboratory.

It's as though the light is actually like a little ball that hits a stationary ball in the laboratory, gives the stationary ball a kick so that stationary ball is now moving and, in the process, the ball that you threw must lose some of its energy. If the energy of light is somehow related to the wavelength and the frequency, then we could explain this phenomenon.

Light might be a bundle of energy that hits an electron, gives it some non-zero speed, and scatters off with a lower energy. That might be what affects the wavelength. This indeed does illustrate well the particle nature of light. Light can be considered to be a bunch of photons, little packages, particles and bundles of energy, which go along collectively. Light of a given wavelength, like red light reflected from a shirt, is a whole bunch of these photons having the same wavelength, but all collectively going along and moving in the same direction, all with about the same wavelength, each being a discreet bundle of energy.

Blue light would also be a bundle of energy but one having a different wavelength or a different frequency. Green light, having an intermediate wavelength, would also be a bundle of energy, but again with a different wavelength, a different frequency.

Max Planck, one of the giants of quantum physics early in the 20th century, quantified this in such a way. He said let light came in packet, and the energy of a given packet would be a little, tiny constant, now known as Planck's constant, times the frequency of the light corresponding to that photon. That is, the photon itself has a frequency and the energy (E) is some little constant (h) times the frequency of the light (v).

$$E = hv$$

Since frequency multiplied by wavelength equals speed, we can replace the frequency in this equation by the speed over the wavelength. This is just an equivalent way of stating the energy of a photon. It's a little constant (h) multiplied by the speed of light (c) divided by the wavelength (λ).

$$E = hc/\lambda$$

Each of these little tiny packets of energy can move along, and if it hits a stationary electron in the laboratory, it can give some of its energy to that electron. What's left then is a photon of lower energy, of longer wavelength, of lower frequency.

The Compton effect cannot be understood in the purely wave description of light. You need the photon description. But then you might say, "Well, what gives?" I thought I showed you an experiment that illustrated the wave nature of light. Light clearly produces an interference pattern when it passes through two little holes in a barrier. Yet here I'm telling you that light is also a particle. Well, which one is it, particle or wave?

You might say, "Well, actually, maybe there's some way of explaining the interference pattern by having particles go through and interact with one another to produce an interference pattern." Maybe you would not necessarily expect a bunch of particles going through the barrier to pile up diametrically opposite the hole in the barrier. This is what you would expect if baseballs were thrown through holes in a barrier. The baseballs would pile up diametrically opposite to the holes. What we observe is that actually you get this interference pattern, but the skeptic might say there's some way in which the different particles can interfere with each other and produce wave-like phenomenon, even though they're really particles.

That's not the way it goes. Because we can send such feeble light through those two holes, we know that only one photon at a time is going through. We can send the light one photon at a time. Send one photon today, wait a week, then send another photon, wait another week, then send a third photon and wait another week. Do this for a few years, and then develop the photograph on which you're recording what the light has registered. You will see the interference pattern shown in this right-hand diagram. You will not see light concentrated in two spots diametrically opposite each of the holes. Rather, you will see the light concentrated in a multitude of spots looking exactly like the interference pattern you would have, had you sent the brilliant light through those holes.

Clearly, the photons are interfering with themselves. A given bundle of light actually goes through each of the two holes simultaneously, breaks itself apart somehow, and then interferes on the other side so that it knows that it is supposed to land in such a way that the ultimate pattern resembles that of the interference of a wave. Yet it goes through both holes, so light is both a particle and a wave.

You might say, "I'm going to fool nature. I'm going to see which hole every photon went through. I'm going to hook up a little gizmo next to each hole that will measure which hole it went through; did it go through hole 1 or did it go through hole 2? Then after doing this experiment, I will look at the interference pattern and surely the interference pattern should be gone, because if a photon goes either through hole one or through hole two, then you must get this kind of a pattern of baseballs going through a barrier."

Indeed, you do; that's what you get. If you measure which hole the photon goes through, you end up getting the distribution that looks like that of particles, of baseballs going through a barrier. If you choose not to measure which hole the photons go through, then you get the interference pattern that is characteristic of waves.

If you choose to measure the light going through the holes, you're treating it as though it were a particle. You're measuring its particle properties and what you're telling the light is that right now, "I'm going to only look at your particle properties." The photon says, "Fine, I'll be a particle", and the wave pattern will disappear. But if you choose not to look which hole the thing went through, then the wave says, "Great, I'll retain my wave properties and I'll produce this interference pattern."

The fact that the observer can actually influence the outcome of the experiment and the fact that the photon is really both a particle and a wave are incredible discoveries, really. But in any given experiment, you can only measure one property or the other, either the wave-like properties—if you don't worry which hole it went through—or the particle-like properties—if you choose to measure which hole it went through; but you cannot measure both simultaneously.

This property of light actually turns out to be a property of normal matter as well, of electrons, protons and people. It's just that it's harder to see with things that we consider particles, such as baseballs and people. But we also have a wave-like property associated with us. Our wavelength, λ, is the same constant, Planck's constant, provided by our mass times our velocity. That quantity, mass times velocity, is known as momentum.

The problem is that typically, for any sort of a macroscopic particle, even for a proton or an electron, the mass is so big that the momentum with any non-zero velocity is enormous. Planck's constant is already so small that Planck's constant divided by the momentum is an exceedingly small number. Hence, the associative wavelength of this particle is tiny and it is difficult to discern the interference properties, the wave-like properties. If the thing isn't moving at all and the wavelength is long, then you can't see the wave-like properties because, in fact, you're not even allowing the thing to move through two holes.

Even matter has this wave-particle duality. It is not restricted to light alone, although it was first discovered in the form of light. All properties of nature, all material objects and all light, has this wave particle duality, and this is the fundamental concept of quantum physics.

Lecture Four
The Fingerprints of Atoms

Scope:

Atoms are the basic constituents of matter. The small nucleus contains neutrons and positively charged protons, and is surrounded by a much larger "cloud" of negatively charged electrons. An ionized atom has lost one or more electrons. One consequence of quantum physics is the discrete electronic energy levels of atoms: only certain energy states are allowed. An electron can jump from a lower energy level to a higher one by absorbing a photon; conversely, a transition from a higher to a lower level releases a photon. Electrons jumping between the allowed energy levels provide a unique "fingerprint" for each neutral or ionized element. Thus, astronomers can use the absorption and emission lines in spectra of distant objects to deduce their composition. The Doppler effect is an enormously important tool in astronomy: spectral lines are shifted from their rest wavelengths if the source and observer are moving toward or away from each other.

Objectives

Upon completion of this lecture, you should be able to:

1. List the main constituents of atoms.

2. Describe the electronic structure of an atom.

3. Discuss the criteria that must be fulfilled if a photon is to be absorbed by an atom.

4. Explain how spectral absorption and emission lines are formed when light passes through a cloud of gas.

5. Summarize how astronomers can determine the chemical composition of a distant object.

6. Describe the Doppler effect and its origin.

7. Calculate the radial velocity of an object relative to an observer, given the observed and rest wavelengths of a specific absorption or emission line in its spectrum.

Outline

I. Astronomers study matter elsewhere in the Universe through analysis of the light that it emits and with which it interacts. We first consider the structure of atoms, the basic constituents of matter.

A. An *atom* consists of a nucleus surrounded by a cloud of electrons. A *molecule* consists of at least two atoms bound together.

1. The atomic nucleus contains positively charged protons and a roughly equal number of uncharged neutrons, all closely packed together. Protons and neutrons have diameters of only about 10^{-13} cm.

2. In a *neutral* atom, the number of negatively charged electrons is *exactly* equal to the number of protons. The electrons form a cloud about 10^{-8} cm in diameter; as noted in Lecture 2, an atom is mostly empty. Each electron has a mass of 9.1×10^{-28} g, only 1/1840 times that of a proton or a neutron.

3. The number of protons determines the type of *element*: hydrogen has one proton, helium has two protons, lithium has three protons, and so on. A convenient arrangement of all these is the *periodic table of the elements*.

B. Different *isotopes* of a given element have the same number of protons, but different numbers of neutrons.

1. By far the most common isotope of hydrogen has zero neutrons, but deuterium (rare) has one neutron, and tritium (very rare) has two neutrons.

2. The most common isotope of helium has two neutrons, but there is a rare lighter isotope that has only one neutron.

3. Different isotopes of the same element have the same *chemical* behavior, which is determined by the number of electrons.

C. Atoms are *ionized* if they have lost one or more electrons.

1. If one electron was lost, the atom is "singly ionized." In the case of hydrogen, this is just a proton.

2. If two electrons were lost, the atom is "doubly ionized," and so on.

3. We will later discuss how atoms can become ionized by collisions with other particles, or by absorption of energetic photons.

D. Although we often think of electrons "orbiting" the nucleus like planets orbiting the Sun, this leads to an inconsistency in classical physics: motion along an orbit should cause the electron to emit radiation (since it accelerates), and it would rapidly spiral into the nucleus as it loses energy. Thus, atoms shouldn't exist!

1. According to quantum physics, electrons instead form a cloud or "probability distribution." Nevertheless, it is sometimes useful to think of electrons in distinct "orbits," as in the model developed by Niels Bohr.

2. An electron can only occupy well-defined, *discrete energy levels* in a given atom, rather than a continuum of levels. Each of these levels can be associated with a particular "orbit" for convenience.

3. Electrons in outer "orbits" (levels) have greater energy than those in lower levels.

4. A given atom is in its *ground state* if all of the electrons are in their lowest possible energy levels.

5. If one or more electrons are not in their lowest possible energy levels, the atom is in an *excited state.*

6. The simplest example is hydrogen: the single electron can be in levels labeled n = 1, 2, 3, etc., with corresponding energies of E_1, E_2, E_3, etc.

II. Light interacts with matter by producing transitions between different electronic energy levels.

A. An electron can "jump" from a low energy level to a higher energy level by absorbing a photon. This destroys the photon.

1. The energy of the absorbed photon must be *exactly* equal to the difference between the two energy levels occupied by the electron.

2. Mathematically, if the initial and final energy levels of the electron are E_2 and E_4 (respectively), and if $\Delta E = E_4 - E_2$ is the difference in energy, then the energy E of the absorbed photon must equal ΔE, and its frequency and wavelength can be calculated from $E = h\nu = hc/\lambda$.

3. If the energy of a photon passing through an atom is *not* equal to the difference between the energy level of an electron and any higher unoccupied level, *nothing* will happen. An electron in the n = 2 level of the hydrogen atom, for example, can absorb a photon having a specific wavelength in the green region, jumping to the n = 4 level. However, a yellow photon cannot be absorbed in this configuration; yellow photons don't have the right energy to cause a transition.

4. An electron cannot take only *part* of the energy of a photon and jump to a higher level, leaving a lower-energy photon; either all or none of the energy is absorbed.

5. A sufficiently energetic photon can completely dislodge an electron from an atom. This process is known as *ionization*, and it can occur with any photon more energetic than the minimum required energy.

B. A cloud of gas containing numerous atoms with an electron in the same initial energy level can absorb many or most of the photons whose energy is *exactly* the amount needed to kick the electron to an allowed higher level.

1. Thus, using the example above, many green photons would be absorbed when a beam of white light is shined through hydrogen gas, if a substantial number of atoms have an electron in the n = 2 level.

2. A spectrum of the light beam that passed through the gas would therefore show a deficit at this green wavelength. This is called an *absorption line*.

3. There may be other absorption lines in the spectrum, due to other transitions from lower to higher electronic energy levels.

C. Electrons prefer to be in low energy levels. Very shortly after being boosted to a higher level by photon absorption, an electron can jump back down to the lower level.

1. This process results in the *emission* of a photon.

2. The photon is released in a *random* direction; there is only a small chance that this will be the direction of the original beam.

3. Hence, in the example discussed above, the green absorption line becomes only slightly "filled in" by emission; most of the emitted photons escape from the cloud of gas in other directions.

4. A spectrum of the gas cloud taken from a direction that differs from that of the original beam of light will therefore show an *emission line* at the same (green) wavelength.

D. Note that the downward jump need not be *directly* to the final energy level, if there are allowed levels between the initial and final levels.

1. Several jumps may occur on the way down, each of which results in the emission of a photon at a different wavelength.

2. The *sum* of the energies of the emitted photons must equal the energy of the photon that would have been emitted had the electron jumped directly to its final level. For example, consider a *hypothetical* atom in which the electron absorbs a blue photon, jumping from the first to the third energy levels. The electron might subsequently jump from the third to the second energy levels, releasing a red photon, and then from the second to the first energy levels, releasing a green photon. The sum of the energies of the emitted green and red photons must equal the energy of the absorbed blue photon.

3. The downward jump may even *bypass* the original energy level completely, if there is a still lower level. This produces a higher-energy photon.

4. Thus, the spectrum of a gas cloud viewed from a direction that differs from that of the original beam of light can consist of many emission lines having different wavelengths.

III. Each neutral element and ionized element produces unique *patterns* of absorption lines or emission lines in a spectrum.

A. With only one electron, the hydrogen atom provides the simplest example. The lowest level (n = 1) has *much* less energy than the next level (n = 2), and progressively higher levels are separated from each other by smaller and smaller amounts of energy.

B. Ultraviolet photons produce transitions from n = 1 to any higher energy level.

    1. The resulting distinctive pattern of absorption lines is called the Lyman series.

    2. Lyman-α is the transition from n = 1 to n = 2, Lyman-β is from n = 1 to n = 3, Lyman-γ is from n = 1 to n = 4, and so on.

C. Visible-light photons produce transitions from n = 2 to any higher energy level.

    1. The resulting pattern of absorption lines is called the Balmer series.

    2. Balmer-α (usually called just Hα) is the transition from n = 2 to n = 3, Balmer-β (usually called just Hβ) is from n = 2 to n = 4, and so on.

D. Infrared photons produce the transitions from n = 3 to any higher energy level.

    1. The resulting pattern of absorption lines is called the Paschen series.

    2. Paschen-α is the transition from n = 3 to n = 4, Paschen-β is from n = 3 to n = 5, etc.

E. Hydrogen produces other series of lines as well, at longer infrared and radio wavelengths.

F. Other atoms produce their own distinctive patterns of lines in a spectrum; one can even distinguish between neutral and ionized atoms. Each has a unique "fingerprint" that can be recognized.

    1. Thus, *spectra* can be used to deduce the chemical compositions of very distant stars and glowing clouds of gas!

    2. This is how we *know* that these objects consist of the same elements that are found on Earth and in the Sun (though not necessarily in the same proportions).

    3. In practice, the patterns of lines of different elements overlap if the spectra are not very spread out. One must disperse (spread) the light as much as possible to distinguish the different patterns, but this is easily done.

IV. The *Doppler effect* is an enormously important tool that allows us to determine the *radial velocity* of an object (i.e., its speed toward or away from us) by measuring the wavelengths of absorption or emission lines in its spectrum.

A. Consider a stationary source that is emitting light waves. The wavelength measured by the laboratory observer is denoted λ_0 ("lambda-nought"), and it is independent of the observer's position relative to the source.

B. Now suppose the source is moving relative to the observer.

    1. Along the direction of motion, the source partially keeps up with its most recently emitted wave crest before it emits another wave crest. Thus, the crests get bunched closer together.

    2. An observer standing along the direction of motion would therefore measure a shorter wavelength λ (i.e., $\lambda < \lambda_0$). This is called a *blueshift,* in the sense that blue light has a shorter wavelength than red light. This terminology is used even if λ_0 corresponds to wavelengths shorter than those of blue light (e.g., ultraviolet or X-rays).

    3. Opposite the direction of motion, the source partially pulls away from its most recently emitted wave crest before it emits another wave crest. Thus, the crests get stretched farther apart.

    4. An observer standing opposite the direction of motion would therefore measure a longer wavelength λ (i.e., $\lambda > \lambda_0$). This is called a *redshift,* in the sense that red light has a longer wavelength than blue light. This terminology is used even if λ_0 corresponds to wavelengths longer than those of red light (e.g., infrared or radio).

    5. Perpendicular to the direction of motion, the spacing of the wave crests is unaffected (at least if the speed of the source is not a significant fraction of the speed of light), and an observer would therefore measure the same wavelength λ (i.e., $\lambda = \lambda_0$). The Doppler effect does not measure such a "transverse velocity," but only a radial velocity.

C. We have all heard the Doppler effect for sound waves: an approaching siren has a high pitch (i.e., high frequency and short wavelength), and as the siren passes by us and recedes the pitch becomes lower (i.e., it swings to lower frequencies and longer wavelengths).

    1. In the case of sound waves, the quantitative (but not qualitative) result slightly depends on whether the source or the observer is moving through the air.

    2. In the case of light waves, the quantitative result depends only on the *relative motion* of the source and observer.

    3. Note that the relationship $\lambda v = c$ still holds for blueshifted or redshifted light. Wavelengths and frequencies change, but the measured speed is *independent* of the motion of the source or the observer.

D. For light waves, the quantitative relationship between λ, λ_0, and v is as follows: $(\lambda - \lambda_0)/\lambda_0 = v/c$, where v is the relative speed between the source and the observer.

    1. This can also be written $\Delta\lambda/\lambda_0 = v/c$, where $\Delta\lambda = \lambda - \lambda_0$, the *difference* between the measured wavelength and the known wavelength if the source and observer were at rest relative to each other.

    2. The above equation is valid only if v is much less than c. As v increases, the approximation becomes worse; by v $= 0.2c$, the error is about 12 percent. An expression from the special theory of relativity must be used at high speeds.

    3. Note that when λ is larger than λ_0, the light is redshifted, so the source and the observer are receding away from each other. Similarly, when λ is smaller than λ_0, the light is blueshifted, so the source and the observer are approaching each other.

    4. The procedure to use with a star, for example, is to obtain its spectrum, recognize a familiar pattern of absorption lines (e.g., the Balmer series), measure the observed wavelengths of an absorption line, and compare it with the known laboratory (rest) wavelength to get $\Delta\lambda$.

    5. For example, if the Hα absorption line is found at $\lambda =$ 6565 Å, and its rest wavelength is known to be $\lambda_0 =$ 6563 Å, we find that $\Delta\lambda = \lambda - \lambda_0 = 2$ Å, so $\Delta\lambda / \lambda_0 = 2$

Å/6563 Å = 3 × 10^{-4}. But we know that this is equal to v/c, so v = (3 × 10^{-4})c = (3 × 10^{-4})(3 × 10^5 km/s) = 90 km/s. Thus, we and the star are moving away from each other at about 90 km/s.

Essential Readings:

Bova, B. *The Beauty of Light.* 1988, Wiley.

Hearnshaw, J. *The Analysis of Starlight.* Cambridge Univ. Press, 1986.

Hey, A., and Walters, P. *The Quantum Universe.* Cambridge University Press, 1987.

Kirkpatrick, L., and Wheeler, G. *Physics: A World View*, 2nd edition. Saunders, 1995.

Questions to Consider:

1. If someone were to say that we can't know the composition of distant stars, since there is no way to perform experiments on them in terrestrial laboratories, how would you respond?

2. Discuss at least one way in which the quantum properties of matter on very small size scales determine the macroscopic properties of matter.

3. Does the Doppler shift depend on the distance between the source of light and the observer?

Lecture Four—Transcript
The Fingerprints of Atoms

I discussed last time how astronomers receive almost all of the information that they get from astronomical objects in the form of the light that they receive. They study this light, plot its spectrum, its brightness versus wavelength or color, and learn about the physical characteristics of that object and about the physical characteristics of the material between a given point and that object.

There are some exceptions. Here is a meteorite, which we received from elsewhere in the Solar System. We weigh it. We can submerge it in water and measure its volume, or pour some acid on it at see how it reacts, and in such a way learn about this thing from elsewhere in the Solar System.

But, in general, all we receive is light, so we would like to learn as much as possible from the clues that light gives us. We would like to use light to the fullest to find out as much as possible about the objects in the Universe and the dark material between objects.

To do that, I have to tell you a little bit about matter, the interaction of light with matter, and how matter produces light. In this lecture, I'll show you how light interacts with matter and produces the fingerprints with which we can identify elements in the Universe. We will find that the things out there are made out of the same sort of stuff we are. I will show you how to use light to deduce these chemical compositions of stars, gases, and things like that.

To do that, let's consider the structure of matter. Matter consists of atoms, and atoms bound together are called molecules. Here, at the left, is the hydrogen atom, the simplest atom. It consists simply of one proton and one electron that are sort of in a cloudy distribution around that proton.

The proton has a positive charge. The electron has a negative charge. They balance each other out to be electrically neutral. The electron is in this cloud roughly 50,000 times the radius of the proton. So, the electron itself isn't huge, but the electron occupies, or defines, a huge volume relative to the size of the proton. The proton is about 2,000 times as massive as an electron, by the way.

This is hydrogen, defined by one proton and one electron. Helium has two protons. There they are, one proton and the second one. In a neutral helium atom, you have two electrons, which balance the charge of the protons. Again, the helium atom is electrically neutral.

The helium nucleus contains, in addition to the protons, two neutral particles, the neutrons. These neutral neutrons help bind the protons together. The protons are positively charged, so if there were nothing there to keep them together, they would go rushing apart from one another. The electric repulsion of the protons would separate them very quickly, so the neutrons are there to sort of glue the nucleus together, and the more protons you have, the more neutrons you need to glue them together.

These elements can be arranged in the famous periodic table according to their atomic number, the number of protons that they contain. Hydrogen has one proton. It's at the left here. Helium has two protons. It is way over at the right. Then there is lithium with three protons, beryllium with four, boron with five, carbon with six, and so on. The vertical columns in this table actually define sets of elements, which behave chemically in similar ways. They're not exactly the same kind of elements, but they behave in similar ways. There are many fascinating aspects of this periodic table, ranging all the way from hydrogen, the lightest element, to the very heavy guys—uranium, and the heavier still, such as lawrencium, berkelium and others.

All of these elements, it turns out, have a particular signature by which they can be recognized. I will describe that signature for you today and show you how it is that we deduce that the rest of the Universe consists of the same sort of stuff as the stuff of which we are made.

Let's look more closely at the nuclei of atoms. Let's strip away the electrons and just look at the central regions. The simplest form of hydrogen consists of only one proton. There it is, all alone. But there is another form of hydrogen, another isotope of hydrogen that has, in addition to the proton, a neutron. This isotope is called deuterium and it is just a form of hydrogen; it is heavy hydrogen. You can denote it by D or by H with a subscript "1", which indicates the number of protons, and a superscript "2", which indicates the number of neutrons plus protons (H_1^2). That's heavy hydrogen.

There's a more rare isotope still, of hydrogen, called tritium (T), which consists of one proton. It has to have one proton, because otherwise it wouldn't be hydrogen, but it has two neutrons. The total number of nucleons, neutrons plus protons, is three, so the superscript to the H would be "3" in this case.

These different isotopes of hydrogen have different nuclear properties because they have different numbers of nucleons, but their chemical properties are the same because it's still the same number of electrons for a neutral atom. It's the electrons that determine molecular bonds and things like that, so only the nucleons differ.

In the case of helium, there are two isotopes. The most common one is called helium-4. It has two protons and two neutrons. There's a light element or a light form of helium called helium-3, which has two protons and only one neutron. Again, these two forms of helium behave chemically the same way, but their nuclear properties differ.

If we look back, then, at neutral atoms, we see an equal number of electrons and protons and variable numbers of neutrons, depending on what kind of isotope you're discussing. Now, an atom can lose an electron either: if it's kicked by another atom, it could just kick the atom away; or if it absorbs energetic light, it can kick the electron away. The atom is then called an ion, or an ionized atom.

Hydrogen can be ionized once. There's only one electron you can lose, and that would leave the proton sitting there all alone. Helium can lose one electron or two electrons. It is either singly ionized, doubly ionized, or neutral, of course.

It turns out that the electrons cannot have any arbitrary energy. They occupy certain orbital levels around the nuclei, not in the sense that they orbit like planets around a star, but rather that they have a particular energy level. These energy levels are fairly well defined. They cannot be any arbitrary number; they can be only certain discrete numbers. We often draw these energy levels as orbits, like planets orbiting the sun, but they're not really orbits in the classical sense. They are simply a way to represent the discrete energy levels.

It turns out that if the electrons orbited the nucleus, they would rapidly spiral into the nucleus and the atom would be destroyed. That is because an electron is a charged particle and, as it accelerates as it moves in a circle or an ellipse around a nucleus, it would emit electromagnetic radiation; charged particles do that if they're accelerating. It would lose energy and spiral in towards the nucleus, just like a satellite orbiting the Earth would lose energy due to friction, for example, against the atmosphere and slowly spiral in towards the surface of the Earth.

Classically, atoms shouldn't even exist. They only exist because of their quantum properties, which dictate these energy levels. The Teaching Company has a course on this, "General Relativity and the Quantum Revolution", which describes it in more detail.

You have these distinct, discrete energy levels and the inner energy levels have lower energy than the outer energy levels. If you were to go from level one to two to three to four, you would have to give the electron energy. The outer orbits have greater energy, but you can only give that electron a discrete amount of energy. If you try to give it an arbitrary amount of energy, it won't necessarily take it. It will only take certain specifically defined amounts of energy according to its electronic structure like this.

An analogy might be a parking meter that has slots for a nickel, a dime and a quarter. Let's say you're only allowed to throw in one coin at this particular parking spot. You can put in a nickel, a dime or a quarter, but you can't put in 13¢. That's not one of the allowed units of money that you can put in. The meter just won't take it. It won't accept 13¢. You can only have several different possibilities, but not any arbitrary possibilities.

What that means in the case of an atom whose electron wants to, perhaps, jump to another state, is that it can only do so when a photon of exactly the right energy, comes in, gets absorbed by the electron, and the electron then takes that energy and jumps to a higher, more outer energy level.

So, it grabs the energy of that photon, and Planck's formula for the energy of the photon, is just Planck's constant times the frequency of the photon. The electron grabs that energy, destroys the photon in the process, and jumps to a higher outer energy level. It will only do that if the photon that's incident upon the atom has energy equal to the difference between two of these possible energy states. If you tried to aim a photon with wrong energy towards that electron, it simply won't be absorbed. It will just pass right through the atom.

Let me illustrate this with the diagram here, which shows the hydrogen atom with an electron in its first excited state. The ground state is the orbit that's closest to the nucleus. The first excited state is the next one out. Here I've got this electron sitting there, and lots of photons are going towards the atom. There's a violet photon, a blue one, a green one, a red one, a burnt orange one, and a red one.

Now, let's suppose, that in moving from the second to the fourth energy level, the electron needs to absorb a green photon. Let's just set things up that way. All these other photons have the wrong energy to do anything. The electron will absorb the green photon. This will propel the electron to the outer energy level, and the other photons will remain unaffected. They simply will pass through.

Let's do a little demonstration of this. I'm an electron sitting around waiting for a photon to come in and, low and behold, a green photon comes my way. There I go. I hop up to a higher energy level, because this photon had exactly the right energy to bring me from my previous state up to this next energy level, or to whatever energy level is the suitable one.

If, instead, a yellow photon had come my way, nothing would have happened. It actually would have passed right through me, not bounced off, of course. But it wouldn't have affected my electronic energy level, because that photon had the wrong amount of energy. It did not correspond to an amount of energy equal to the difference between my energy level and any other allowed energy level. Only certain photons will be accepted, only those that have the right energy; the other ones will be unaffected.

Going back now to this diagram, we ask, "What will happen to this electron once it's in the higher energy level?" It turns out that electrons don't like being in higher energy levels for very long. They're kind of lazy things. They like to jump back down to low energy levels, preferably the lowest ground state level. What actually happens in that case is that the photons go zipping back down after a very short amount of time, typically a hundred-millionth of a second, or something, to a lower level. It doesn't have to be the same one from which they came. It can be a different one, but certainly the one from which they came is a possibility.

In any case, in a downward jump, an electron gives up some of its energy, because it goes to a state of lower energy and, hence, must emit a photon. It radiates a photon with energy, $E = h\nu$, corresponding to the difference in energy between two of these levels. That is called the emission of a photon.

Let's go back to this hydrogen atom here. Suppose you get a whole bunch of atoms in gas and you have lots of photons coming along; there are blue ones, green ones, orange ones, and infrared ones. What's going to happen? If there is a bunch of electrons, or a bunch of atoms whose electrons are in this second energy level, they're just ready to absorb green photons. They're sort of hungry for green photons.

They will absorb those green photons, or at least a fair fraction of the atoms will absorb those photons and will jump up to higher energy levels. So, a spectrum of the gas, or more precisely a spectrum of the light, going through that gas, will have green photons preferentially missing. It will have a deficit of green photons relative to the other ones because those atoms absorbed the green photons. The spectrum would look like this. Plotting brightness versus color or wavelength, you'd have the normal curve corresponding to the incident radiation, whatever light was passing through that gas, but there will be a deficit of intensity, a deficit of photons and a less bright light at the particular wavelength of those green photons that were absorbed by that gas. Some of the atoms in that gas will have stolen those photons, so there will be an absorption line.

That absorption line will correspond to energy exactly equal to the energy difference between the two levels. ΔE, the difference in energy between the two levels, will be E_4 minus E_2 and that will equal the energy of the photon given by Planck's constant times the frequency of the photon. Since frequency multiplied by wavelength is just the speed of light, we can replace frequency here by the speed of light over the wavelength of the photon.

The energy of those missing photons, the energy associated with that absorption line, corresponds to a wavelength given by hc/λ. What you really do in practice is measure the wavelength where the photons are missing, and calculate the energy of those missing photons. That's related, then, to the structure of the atom that did the absorption.

You might say, "Wait a minute. Aren't all those electrons which jumped up to a higher energy level going to go back down to a lower energy level, perhaps the one from which they came? If so, shouldn't they fill in the absorption line? After all, if all of the electrons jump up to a higher energy level by stealing photons, won't they just re-

release those photons and allow them to go merrily on their way, thereby filling in that absorption line?"

That actually doesn't happen for two reasons. The first, as shown here, is that the emission of the photon occurs in any random direction. If, I'm the atoms in the gas, and the light is coming from over there, I absorb these green photons. An observer over there is measuring the light passing through me and I claim that observer would measure a deficit of green photons. The reason is that I will re-emit those green photons in random directions, not necessarily in the direction that they were going to begin with; I will not completely fill in the absorption line. A little bit of it will be filled in by the random photons that I emit in that same direction, but most of the photons that I emit will be in other directions, simply because there's more space out there than in the direction in which they were going initially.

The other reason that absorption line doesn't get filled in completely is that several jumps can occur to various levels, if allowed. For example, when the electron is in this fourth energy level, it could jump to a third one, or to a second one. It could go from four to three, and then from three to two, and then, say, from two to one. But it doesn't necessarily have to go from four to two. So, a green photon that was initially absorbed—or a blue photon, or whatever color it had—can be transformed into several photons of lower energy once they get re-emitted, as long as the sum of those energies is equal the energy of the absorbed photon.

When this absorption occurs, even the photon gets absorbed completely, or it doesn't get absorbed at all. The electron can't take part of the energy of the photon, jump up to a higher energy level and leave the rest in the form of a photon of lower energy or longer wavelength. You can only take the whole photon or none of it. You can't cut the quarter in half, if we go back to our parking meter example.

Now, let's illustrate this by having you throw me a blue photon. Let me give you yet another photon as well. If you throw me the blue photon, I'll go from this state up to this one because I'm supposing that I set up the experiment so that the difference in energy level between the floor and this higher box is in this case exactly equal to the energy of a blue photon. I can then jump not directly back down from the position in which I started, but I can go in stages. I can first jump to this level, releasing a red photon, which has lower energy than a blue photon, and then to the original level releasing a green photon.

If the sum of the energies of the green and red photons were equal to the energy of the blue photon, that got me to the higher state to begin with, that's an allowed thing to do; the atom can do that. So, you see, the original blue photon was regenerated; but in the form of a green and a red one, the sum of whose energies equaled that of the blue one.

There's one other physical process that can occur. Suppose an ultraviolet photon comes in—suppose a really high-energy photon comes in—so that it gives me so much energy that there is no allowed orbit for me to go into. It's such an energetic photon that it completely kicks me away from the atom. Throw me such a photon; that's an ultraviolet photon. I grab it—I'm the electron—and now I just go wandering around every which way I want. I'm no longer bound to the nucleus of the atom. I can pursue any old path that I want, depending on my interactions with other particles in the gas. I'm no longer bound in any sort of an orbital level to that atom. That process is called ionization. I have become ionized, and I am now a free electron, free to pursue whatever path I want.

This process of ionization is quite important in gases around hot stars, because hot stars produce a lot of ultraviolet photons. Those photons go around and ionize the atoms and cause a whole bunch of free electrons to be produced. Those free electrons can then do all sorts of things. They can recombine with positive charges, with atomic nuclei and, in so doing will release photons. They will recombine, in some cases, to outer energy levels and cascade down in steps to lower energy levels. So, an ultraviolet photon can be converted, or its energy can be converted, into a whole bunch of lower energy photons, green ones, infrared ones, and things like that, by cascading down through these different levels. We often see clouds of gas glowing around hot stars due to this process of ionization and recombination.

What, then, would one see if one were near a star emitting a continuous spectrum? I'll talk later on about how a continuous spectrum is formed, but basically hot opaque objects have a lot of interactions among their particles, and they sort of smear out all the different energy levels. What you get is a continuum of colors, a continuum of emitted wavelengths.

An observer looking at a star or a hot source of continuous radiation would see a smooth curve plotting brightness versus wavelength. There would just be a smooth curve, with no absorption lines and no emission lines.

But, what would an observer see staring through a cloud of colder gas towards the hot source of this continuum spectrum? The colder gas will absorb some of the photons from this source. They will be absorbed by gas having electrons in the proper energy levels to do the absorption. Here, in the green part of the spectrum, you might get a deficit of photons. In the yellow part you might get a deficit and several more deficits in the red part. There will be these absorption lines imprinted upon the spectrum, depending on the elements that happen to be in that cloud of gas.

If you can recognize the pattern of lines, you will deduce that that cloud of gas contains those elements. We're getting to the key of how astronomers learn what sort of things are out there.

If, on the other hand, you're an observer who is looking at the cloud, not in a direction towards the source of the continuum, but rather in some other direction, just looking at this cloud sitting out there in space, what will you see? You will see emission lines. You will not see a continuum, because this cloud does not emit a continuum, at least not visible wavelengths, but it does emit photons as a consequence of all these electrons in upper levels jumping back down to the lower levels. They jump down and they re-emit photons in random directions. You would see those photons coming from the cloud of gas, if you're observing the cloud from a random direction.

You see a bright emission line spectrum in this case; a continuum with absorption lines if you're staring at the hot source; and if you were looking only at the hot source, not through the cloud of gas, you would see only a continuum.

Hydrogen has many possible energy levels. Here they are shown sort of schematically. There's the lowest one down there—it's a bit hard to see—and the second one, third one, fourth one, and so on. They look nearly equally spaced here, but that's not really the case. They're spaced by different amounts, but still an electron can go from the first energy level to the second one. That, it turns out, requires an ultraviolet photon. Or it can go from the first energy level to the third one, and that also requires an ultraviolet photon. It's called Lyman-β. The first one was called Lyman-α. This whole ultraviolet series will be called the Lyman series. An electron going from the first energy level to the third energy level is a Lyman-γ photon. That's also an ultraviolet photon, and so on.

These photons that produce absorptions from the lowest energy level of hydrogen are very energetic photons because that lowest energy level is very tightly bound to the proton. It has a very low energy, and you have to give it a large amount of energy to get that electron to go up to a higher energy level. It requires an ultraviolet photon to do that, and that series of photons that produces those transitions are called the Lyman photons.

If, instead, the electron is in the second energy level, then it can absorb a photon to go to the third energy level, and that would be a photon in the red part of the spectrum. It's called the Balmer-α, or simply Hα, line of hydrogen because the first spectra ever to be examined of stars were visible spectra, not ultraviolet spectra, and they were given the name H, just because that was the only thing that was known. Hα: now it's known as Balmer-α as well.

From the second energy level to the fourth energy level requires an Hβ photon—a somewhat more energetic photon, still in the visible part of the spectrum—but more energetic. Going from the second energy level to the third one requires a yet more energetic photon. It's called an Hγ photon. And, to the fourth level, requires a still more energetic photon.

Now, the electron could just as well start out in the third energy level. You're beginning to see the pattern here. Going up to the fourth level would require a photon. It happens to be an infrared photon. Going to the fifth level requires a somewhat more energetic infrared photon, and so on.

We can perhaps better represent the relative spacing of the levels in the hydrogen atom in this figure here, where you see the energy plotted in units known as electron volts. It doesn't really matter what they are, it's just the relative spacing here that matters, and it's shown correctly. The ground state, the lowest energy level of the electron in the hydrogen atom, is way down here and we can define its energy to be zero. Relative to that zero, the second orbital level has an energy of 10 electron volts; the third one has an energy of 12, and so on.

Here we have the process in reverse; the arrows are shown going from up to down. So we're showing the emission process. Here are the Lyman series of photons. Electrons that jump from any energy level to the lowest, or first, energy level produce them, this ultraviolet series of lines known as the Lyman series.

If, instead, electrons are jumping from any energy level to the second energy level, those are visible photons. Those are the Balmer series of hydrogen. If they are going from any energy level to the third energy level, then that's called the Paschen series. Those are infrared photons. Going from any energy level to the fourth level is even farther into the infrared. That's the Brackett series.

This green region here denotes the continuum, the region where an electron is not bound to the atom anymore. If you gave an electron 13.6 electron volts of energy, and it was initially in the ground state, it would become an ionized atom. That is, the electron would completely free itself from the atom and wander around in the manner that I indicated a few minutes ago.

Let's look, then, at the spectrum that we would get of a continuous light source as viewed through a cold cloud of hydrogen gas. We're plotting brightness versus color, or wavelength. The energy increases as the wavelength decreases, so ultraviolet photons have high energy and infrared photons have low energy, or long wavelength.

The initially continuous spectrum gets chopped up a little bit into these absorption lines. Here in the ultraviolet wavelengths, you see the Lyman series: Lyman-α, β, γ, δ, ε, and so on. These correspond to electrons jumping from the first energy level up to any other level.

In the visible part of the spectrum, you see the Balmer series: α, β, γ, δ, ε, corresponding to electrons jumping from the second energy level up to any other energy level.

In the infrared part of the spectrum—we don't quite show Paschen-α here—it would be farther to the infrared (longer wavelengths). Then, there is Paschen-β, γ, δ, again corresponding to electrons jumping from the third level up to a higher energy level.

The point here is not to memorize these designations—Lyman, Balmer, and Paschen—or the wavelengths of the lines. The point is to see that there are patterns. These patterns are distinct to the hydrogen atom. No other atom has a pattern with exactly the same spacing as the Balmer series or the Lyman series or the Paschen series, or any other series that the hydrogen atom is able to produce. That is a fingerprint of the hydrogen atom. If you see that kind of spectrum, you can deduce that there is hydrogen either in the star that emitted the light, or in the gas along the way between the star and the observer.

It turns out there is a way that we can tell the difference, whether the absorptions are coming from the star or from gas between Earth and the star. I'll discuss that later. But the point is that we can tell that there was hydrogen somewhere along the way and we can actually figure out where along the way it was.

This means that we can identify hydrogen in that star. Other elements have other distinct patterns of lines. Indeed, the ionized forms of those elements have their own distinct patterns of lines. Singly ionized iron has a different pattern than neutral iron. Doubly ionized iron has a different pattern still. Every single element and every ionization stage of that element has a different pattern. It is exactly like a fingerprint. No two elements and no two ions of those elements have the same pattern. All atoms of neutral calcium have the same pattern, but no two ions of those elements have the same pattern.

This slide right here shows the spectra produced by different gases. At the top, we have mercury. You see it shows emission lines, in this case because it's a hot gas, here in the red part of the spectrum, a few in the orange part and in the green part. Sodium has a different pattern of lines, a pair of strong lines in the yellow-orange part of the spectrum. Helium has yet another pattern still. Hydrogen, which is the element I've been discussing, has a very simple pattern, a line here in the red, another fainter line down in the bluish-green part of the spectrum, and then some more in the violet part of the spectrum.

You can see that these are different patterns. Any trained spectroscopist seeing those patterns would be able to tell you that he/she is looking at mercury, or sodium, or helium, or hydrogen.

In a similar way, then, when we look at a cloud of gas excited and ionized by hot stars, such as in the Orion nebula, which is in the sword of the hunter Orion; we see patterns of lines corresponding to different elements. We see oxygen, calcium, nitrogen, magnesium, and hydrogen. We see all the lines that correspond to elements that we know here in our laboratories. We see the same kind of stuff.

It's interesting that, in one case, by observing an astronomical object, an element, hellion, was first discovered. Helion was seen in the spectrum of the sun and no one really recognized what produced those absorption lines. Later, it was realized that there must be a new element and, in fact, it is now called helion, after Helios, the Sun. Later, in laboratory gases, the spectrum was reproduced. It's not that the Sun consists of something totally different; it consists of a gas that we should have known about here on Earth, but we didn't know about it at that time.

The things out there consist of the same sort of stuff as the things here. This is one of the most interesting realizations that astronomers have made. This is how we know and can say, with essentially absolute certainty, that the stars contain the same kinds of elements that we are used to. We don't have a completely different periodic table out there. It's not some weird stuff that we have no knowledge of here. It's the same kinds of atoms; at least those that emit light are the same kinds of atoms. We will see later on that there is evidence for dark matter in the Universe, and that may well be something different.

Now, let me tell you about a very important aspect of light, and that is the Doppler effect. We can tell whether a source of radiation is moving towards us or away from us by looking at the wavelength of the light it emits. This Doppler effect will turn out to be very similar to what we hear audibly when a siren approaches us or recedes from us.

Consider a stationary source emitting a wave with a particular wavelength, shown here. I just joined the crests of the waves. The crests correspond to these circles here. The wavelength is fixed to an observer, which is at rest with respect to the source. We will call that wavelength λ_0, and the rest, wavelength of the source.

Now, consider the situation from the perspective of an observer that's looking at the source, and either moving towards the source, or the source is moving towards the observer. It doesn't matter which one it is; it's the relative motion that matters. In the time interval between the emission of the first crest and the emission of the second crest, the source will have moved towards observer A. That means that the second crest, when it is emitted, will already be partly along its way. It will have partly caught up with the first crest, simply because the source already moved in that direction. Similarly, the third one, when it's emitted, will already be part of the way along.

The observer would observe these crests to be squished together. They would have a shorter wavelength than that measured by an observer at rest, with respect to the source, because they are squished together—that we call a blue shift, a squishing of the wavelengths from the red part of the spectrum toward the blue. We use that term even if we're already talking about very blue photons, radio photons or X ray photons. It's not the precise color that matters; it's the direction of the shift. If you're shifting from longer wavelengths to shorter wavelengths, we call that a blue shift.

From the perspective of an observer from whom the source is receding, we would have the following situation; in the interval between the emission of the first crest and the second crest, the source will have receded from the observer. The wavelength will be increased, because by the time the second crest is emitted, it will be a greater distance away from the observer. This will be true of all successive crests, so the observed wavelength for an observer who sees the source receding will be longer, or red-shifted. So this is a longer wavelength than the rest wavelength.

To an observer looking at the source, from a perpendicular direction, so that the source is neither moving towards nor away from the observer, but rather tangentially to the line of sight, the measured wavelength will be unaffected. It will be λ_0. It will be the same as that observed by the observer at rest. That's because the source is not moving towards the observer or away from the observer, so there is not stretching or squishing of the waves.

You can see that this allows us to determine the direction of motion of a light source and its speed. It's almost exactly like a siren. A siren approaching has a high pitch and receding has a low pitch. We've all heard that affect when an ambulance or a siren goes by. That's the Doppler effect.

It's similar for light as it is for sound. In the case of sound, it does matter a little bit whether the source or the observer is moving. For light it doesn't matter; for sound it matters a little bit, but the principal is essentially the same.

Now let's look at the spectrum of a star, brightness plotted against wavelength (color). Suppose this star is not moving towards us or away from us. Its radial velocity, radial along the line of sight, is zero. The pattern of hydrogen absorption lines would be the same as what we always observe, and the wavelengths at which those absorption lines occur would be the same as in a laboratory gas at rest. I denote those wavelengths by these little tip marks here. No shift.

Now suppose the star moves towards us. The same pattern of lines would be observed, but each of those lines would be shifted slightly towards bluer wavelengths, with the magnitude of the shift being dependent on the speed of the source. Every single one of these things is shifted.

Now suppose the star moves away from us. Again, we'd see the same pattern that we can unambiguously associate with hydrogen, but that whole pattern would be shifted towards redder wavelengths. It would be a red shift and that would tell us that the motion of the star is away from us.

To determine the speed towards or away, we simply measure the amount of the shift: $\Delta\lambda$. The observed wavelength is here. The wavelength it would have had at rest is λ_0. It's slightly bluer in this case I'm showing here (a red shift). So this is $\Delta\lambda$—you can measure that. λ observed (the observed wavelength) minus the rest wavelength—λ_0—is $\Delta\lambda$. If we divide that quantity by the rest wavelength (λ_0) it turns out that that quantity, $\Delta\lambda/\lambda_0$, is approximately equal to the speed of the source, divided by the speed of light.

This very simple formula works, as long as the speed of the source or the observer is much less than the speed of light. For speeds getting comparable to the speed of light, or even 10 percent of the speed of light, you have to use a more accurate relativistic formula given by Einstein's theory of relativity.

For small speeds, a very simple formula holds:

$$\Delta\lambda/\lambda_0 = v/c.$$

Let's take an example. Suppose we observe a star whose hydrogen alpha line, the red line, is shifted toward the red by two angstrom units. This little shift here, $\Delta\lambda$, is two. It's observed at a wavelength of 6,565 angstroms. If you happen to know that the rest wavelength is 6,563 (You don't have to memorize this, you can just look it up in a book.), then you can compute $\Delta\lambda$ to angstroms. Divide by λ_0, which is 6,563, and the result is 3×10^{-4}. That's this quantity—$\Delta\lambda/\lambda_0$.

Now, just multiply by the speed of light to get the speed with which the star is moving away from you; 3×10^{-4} multiplied by the speed of light (3×10^{5} kilometers per second) is about 90 kilometers per second. So, we can conclude that the star is moving away from us, because its spectrum is red-shifted, and that the speed with which it's moving away is 90 kilometers per second, because we've measured $\Delta\lambda$.

One can see that this is a very good technique with which one can measure the speeds of nearby stars, distant stars, very different galaxies or anything that emits light having a spectrum that one can recognize. One can get speeds in this manner.

Lecture Five
Tools of the Trade

Scope:

Astronomers want to gather as much light as possible from a given object, and perform quantitative studies of it. Most modern detectors are electronic gadgets that store information in digital form for convenient computer analysis. Sensitive charge-coupled devices, in particular, are exceedingly useful. There are two main types of telescopes, refracting and reflecting, the latter now being far more common than the former. Telescopes collect light quickly and in large quantities; the primary lens (or mirror) should therefore be as big as possible. They also increase the amount of detail that can be seen in an object, although ground-based observations are generally limited by atmospheric turbulence. The effective clarity can be improved by measuring the turbulence and making appropriate corrections, or by combining the signals from more than one telescope in a special manner. The largest modern research telescopes are based on clever new designs that greatly decrease costs.

Objectives

Upon completion of this lecture, you should be able to:

1. Summarize the methods used by astronomers to detect and study light.

2. Sketch the paths that light rays follow in different types of telescopes.

3. State the main purposes of telescopes.

4. Calculate the relative light-gathering power of two telescopes, given their diameters.

5. Describe what generally limits the amount of detail seen in celestial objects with ground-based optical telescopes.

6. Explain why radio telescopes are much larger than optical telescopes.

Outline

I. Since light is so important to astronomers, they want to collect as much of it as possible from a given object, and quantitatively study it in great detail.

   A. In the early history of astronomy, all observations were done with the unaided eye, but this is now almost never the case among professional astronomers.

   B. Telescopes are used to gather more light and to provide greater clarity.

   C. Light is recorded with electronic detectors, which are more sensitive than eyes and provide more quantitative measurements than eyes.

   D. Long exposures make it possible to see fainter stars; the eye/brain combination distinguishes a new image about 30 times per second.

   E. Spectrographs and other devices are used to analyze the light in greater detail.

   F. A variety of telescopes on Earth and in space are used to collect light throughout the electromagnetic spectrum, not just visible light.

   G. Computers are essential for thorough quantitative analysis of light.

II. Advances in observational astronomy have been driven by detector technology as much as by increases in telescope size.

   A. At visual wavelengths, for example, the use of photographic emulsions (generally mounted on glass "plates" for stability) provided a great improvement over the human eye.

      1. Long exposures are possible, making faint objects visible.

      2. Many stars over a wide field of view can be recorded simultaneously.

      3. The data are stored for subsequent analysis, and archiving is easy.

      4. Quantitative measurements can be made.

B. Various electronic devices were gradually developed and now supersede plates for most purposes.

  1. By far the most frequently used detectors are CCDs (charge-coupled devices, like those used in video camera recorders).

  2. These consist of a semi-conductor "chip" with a very large number of "pixels" (picture elements). Typical sizes of CCDs in the late 1990s are 2048 × 2048 pixels.

  3. Each pixel develops an electric charge as light hits it, and the amount of charge per pixel is measured at the end of the exposure.

  4. CCDs have the following advantages over photographic plates.

   a. The response of a CCD is linear—that is, if you double the exposure time, or look at a star twice as bright as another star, there will twice as much charge. This turns out to be important for accurate subtraction of unwanted contaminants (e.g., moonlight).

   b. CCDs are extremely sensitive—up to 80 percent of the incoming photons are detected, as compared with 1-2 percent for photographic plates or human eyes.

   c. CCDs have a wide dynamic range—very faint and bright stars can be measured in a given image.

   d. The output of CCDs is digital, and hence is immediately suitable for computer analysis.

III. Telescopes serve at least two useful purposes.

  A. Their main purpose is to collect light quickly and in large quantities.

  1. Light rays from a distant object are essentially parallel and hit all parts of the exposed face of the Earth.

  2. The primary mirror or lens of a telescope acts as a gigantic eye pupil that intercepts the light rays.

  3. The larger its area, the more light it will collect in a given time, allowing fainter objects to be seen. (The length of the telescope tube is irrelevant to the light-gathering power.)

  4. The area of a circle is proportional to the square of its radius r (or diameter D = 2r): $A = \pi r^2 = \pi (D/2)^2 = \pi D^2/4$.

5. Therefore, the ratio of the areas of two telescopes with circular mirrors of diameter D_1 and D_2 is given by $A_2/A_1 = D_2^2/D_1^2 = (D_2/D_1)^2$.

6. Suppose $D_2 = 4$ m (a typical size for a large telescope in the 1990s), and $D_1 = 4$ mm $= 0.004$ m (as for the pupil opening of a typical dilated eye). The ratio of areas is $(D_2/D_1)^2 = (4 \text{ m}/0.004 \text{ m})^2 = 1000^2 = 10^6$. Thus, looking through the eyepiece of such a telescope, one could see stars a million times fainter than with the unaided eye!

7. By attaching a detector to the telescope, the exposure time can be made very long, making even fainter stars visible.

8. Some detectors, such as CCDs, are far more sensitive than eyes, and detect most of the photons that hit them.

9. With large telescopes, long exposures, and high-quality CCDs, objects over 10^9 (a billion) times fainter than the limit of the unaided eye have been detected.

B. Telescopes also improve the clarity with which objects are seen: they have higher *angular resolution* (the ability to see fine detail) than the human eye.

   1. Angular measure is important in astronomy.

      a. The full circle is divided into 360 degrees (360°). The Moon and the Sun each subtend (cover) about ½°.

      b. Each degree consists of 60 arc minutes (60').

      c. Each minute of arc consists of 60 arc seconds (60").

      d. A second of arc is very small—approximately the angle subtended by a dime viewed from a distance of 3.7 km.

      e. One can also use radians for angular measure. There are 2π radians in 360°, so $1" = 1/206265$ radian.

      f. If the angular size (θ) of an object is measured in radians, and if the object appears small in the sky, then the physical size (s) is given by the distance (d) multiplied by the angular size: $s = d\theta$. This is known as the small-angle formula.

   2. If two point-like objects are closer together than 1-2 arc minutes, the unaided eye will perceive them as only one object because their individual "blur circles" merge together.

3. With a telescope, the size of the individual blur circles decreases, and the objects become resolved.

4. The angular size of the blur circle is proportional to λ/D, where λ is the observation wavelength and D is the diameter of the lens or mirror. Hence, in principle, large telescopes are able to resolve finer details than small telescopes (at a given wavelength).

5. In practice, Earth's atmosphere blurs starlight: layers of air with different densities move in a turbulent way relative to each other, and the rays of light bend in different directions. This is related to the twinkling of light.

6. The angular resolution of telescopes larger than 20-30 cm is limited by the blurring effects of the atmosphere (typically 1 arc second, and rarely smaller than 1/3 arc second), not by the size of the mirror or lens; thus, even bigger ground-based telescopes do not give clearer images.

7. There are exceptions to this limitation.

   a. Images of bright objects can be taken with very short exposures in quick succession, and computer processing can remove much of the blurring because the instantaneous images have high resolution. This technique is called "speckle interferometry."

   b. If there is a bright star next to the object of interest, light from this star can be monitored, and rapid changes can be made to a deformable mirror in the telescope so as to produce a very sharp image of the star. The object next to the star will then also appear sharp. This technique is called "adaptive optics."

   c. If there is no bright star next to the object of interest, an artificial star can be produced by shining a laser beam up and exciting a layer of sodium atoms in the upper atmosphere. Light from this artificial star is monitored, as above.

IV. Telescopes come in two main types and several different subtypes.

   A. Refracting telescopes use a lens to collect light, bend (refract) it, and bring it to a focus.

      1. They were invented in Holland around the year 1600.

2. Galileo. Galileo heard of the idea and built his own refractor in 1609. He was the first to make and interpret systematic astronomical observations with a telescope.

3. The focal length is the distance between the lens and the focus, for parallel incident light rays. The light rays reaching us from a distant star are essentially parallel. Consider light rays diverging spherically from an object. The great the object's distance, the more it will seem like the rays reaching our telescope are parallel, since the telescope diameter subtends a very small angle as viewed from the object.

4. A CCD or other detector can be placed at the focus to record the light.

5. An eyepiece is used to magnify the image when looking with the eye.

6. Each "monocular" in a pair of binoculars is a refracting telescope.

7. Refractors have a number of undesirable characteristics.
   a. They suffer from chromatic aberration: light of different wavelengths is brought to different foci. (The focus is closest to the lens for short wavelengths.) This produces a fuzzy image unless a filter is used to transmit only one color.
   b. An additional lens must be installed to partially correct for chromatic aberration. Thus, there are many surfaces to grind, increasing the cost.
   c. Some of the light gets absorbed when passing through the lenses. Also, bubbles in the lenses can affect the image.
   d. The lenses must be supported by their edges, and they tend to sag in the middle, creating distortions in the final image.
   e. The focal length is very large, so the telescope tube is long and heavy.

8. Because of these difficulties, large refractors are no longer being built. The two biggest, dating from about a century ago, are the Lick Observatory 36-inch refractor (under which the donor, James Lick, is buried), and the Yerkes Observatory 40-inch refractor.

B. Reflecting telescopes use a mirror to collect light, reflect it, and bring it to a focus.

   1. Isaac Newton invented the reflecting telescope around the year 1670.

   2. Since the angle of reflection is independent of wavelength, there is no chromatic aberration.

   3. A detector can be placed at the prime focus of the telescope, within the tube.

   4. More commonly, a curved secondary mirror is placed in the tube, and light is reflected back through a central hole in the primary mirror to a mounted instrument. This is called a Cassegrain telescope.

   5. Another configuration, often used in amateur telescopes, is to place a flat secondary mirror in the tube, reflecting light in a perpendicular direction through a hole in the tube. This is called a Newtonian telescope.

   6. Note that the secondary mirror blocks some of the incoming light from an object, making the object look somewhat fainter than in the unblocked case, but it doesn't produce a "hole" in the image (e.g., a hole in Jupiter). Each little part of the primary mirror produces a *complete* (but faint) image of the object.

   7. The simplest curved mirror to construct is a section of a sphere, but it suffers from spherical aberration: parallel rays of light are reflected to different foci, depending on their distance from the center of the mirror. This produces a fuzzy image. The original Hubble Space Telescope had this problem to some extent.

   8. One solution is to make the mirror parabolic, to get a single focus.

C. Schmidt telescopes combine features of reflectors and refractors.

   1. They have a spherical primary mirror, and a corrector lens near the top of the tube.

   2. Photographic plates are placed at the prime focus.

   3. Photographs can be obtained over a much wider field of view than with conventional reflectors.

    4. Schmidt-Cassegrain telescopes are a modification of this design: light passes through a hole in the primary mirror to the eyepiece. These are very compact, and popular among amateur astronomers.

D. From 1948 to the early 1990s, the world's largest telescope of superior quality was the 5 m Hale reflector at Palomar Observatory.

    1. A Russian 6 m telescope was completed in 1976, but it didn't work as well.

    2. Most efforts during those decades were directed toward the improvement of detectors.

    3. When CCDs reached efficiencies of 50-80 percent, the only way to gather more light was to make larger telescopes.

    4. Conventional designs are expensive; the primary mirror must be very thick to maintain its proper shape, and the support structure is bulky, especially with long focal lengths.

E. In the 1990s, new technology was developed that greatly reduced the cost of huge telescopes.

    1. The first major advance was the two Keck Observatory 10 m telescopes on Mauna Kea volcano in Hawaii, the world's largest optical telescopes at the time of writing (mid-1998). These were conceived and funded by the University of California and the California Institute of Technology. (The University of Hawaii, and more recently NASA, also became partners.)

    2. The primary mirror of each Keck telescope consists of 36 thin, lightweight, hexagonal segments arranged in a honeycomb pattern. The focal length is very short.

    3. Devices behind the segments automatically and continually adjust their positions (in real time, while observing) to maintain the correct overall shape.

    4. Another novel technique, developed at the University of Arizona, is to make a single thin mirror by spinning molten glass until it achieves the proper shape, and then allow it to cool. Several such telescopes, typically 8 m in diameter, were under construction in 1998.

    5. Rigidity is provided by a honeycomb (mostly hollow, and therefore lightweight) structure behind the mirror.

6. A consortium of European nations is building four 8-m telescopes in Chile that will eventually be linked together and operate as one telescope.
7. Each mirror is single and thin, and the proper overall shape is continually maintained (while observing) with a series of devices behind it.

V. Ground-based radio telescopes have also played an important role in astronomy.

A. They must be made very large, to provide clear images.
   1. Recall that the angular size of an object's blur circle is proportional to λ/D. Since radio wavelengths are so large, D must be large to compensate.
   2. The Arecibo radio telescope in Puerto Rico is the single largest radio telescope, 305 meters in diameter.
   3. Radio telescopes are always reflectors, and the detectors are at the prime focus.
   4. The reflecting dish can be a wire mesh; the long radio waves don't notice the holes.

B. Signals from two or more separate telescopes can be combined to form a single image with very high resolution.
   1. This technique is known as interferometry: the waves collected by the different dishes interfere with each other, and the object's structure can be deciphered from the pattern.
   2. The effective diameter of such a telescope is the largest spacing between the dishes. Thus, excellent clarity is achieved.
   3. However, the light-gathering power is still determined by the area of the dishes themselves.
   4. The Very Large Array in New Mexico consists of 27 dishes in a Y-shaped pattern.
   5. Signals detected from very widely spaced radio telescopes (e.g., on different continents) can be combined to produce astronomical images with extremely high angular resolution—better than 0.001 arc second. This is called Very Long Baseline Interferometry (VLBI).
   6. Since the interference pattern depends on the exact spacing between the telescopes, VLBI also provides accurate measurements of continental drift.

Essential Reading:

Bunge, R. "Dawn of a New Era: Big Scopes." In *Astronomy* magazine, August 1993, p. 49.

Learner, R. *Astronomy Through the Telescope.* Van Nostrand Reinhold, 1981.

McLean, I. S. *Electronic Imaging in Astronomy: Detectors and Instrumentation.* Wiley, 1997.

Questions to Consider:

1. Is it a coincidence that major improvements in astronomical detectors were made at nearly the same time as the electronics and computer revolution that began in the late 1970s?

2. Does the hole in the center of the mirror in a Cassegrain telescope produce a hole in the object that is being viewed?

3. Telescopes are often advertised according to the amount by which they magnify the apparent size of an image. Do you think this magnification is very relevant when looking at stars?

Lecture Five—Transcript
Tools of the Trade

Astronomers, to study objects in the distant parts of the universe, want to gather as much light as possible and study it in all possible ways to glean as much information as possible about the physics, about the objects, which are emitting the light. We do this by using telescopes to gain more light and to improve clarity. We also use electronic detectors, which are sensitive and provide a quantitative measure of how much light is being emitted by an object. We use long exposure times to increase the quantity of light that's detected. Our own eyes, for example, register a new image roughly 30 times per second, so you don't really expose a long time before moving on to a new view of the object that you're observing. With long exposures, you could see fainter objects because the light would store up.

We use machines called spectrographs to analyze the light and produce a spectrum, or plot of brightness versus wavelength. Such a plot, as we saw last time, reveals what sorts of elements are in the object that's emitting the light and whether the object is moving towards us or away from us, as indicated by the Doppler shift.

We want to view not only visible light, but also ultraviolet wavelengths, X rays, gamma rays (that is, light or electromagnetic radiation that's a shorter wavelength than visible light). We would also like to look at infrared rays and radio waves (waves that are a little longer than visible light), because they, too, provide clues to the nature of the objects that we are observing. If possible, we want to view the entire electromagnetic spectrum from an object.

Finally, we want to use computers for a quantitative analysis of the light. Gone are the days when we just look at the stars and say, "That one looks red and that one looks blue." We want to know how red it is, how blue it is, what sort of absorption lines there are, and precisely how much they are shifted. We want to analyze those precise shifts and the relationships between the different wavelengths with computers, in order to discern as much as possible about the nature of the object that is producing the light and the nature of the objects that might be between us and that light-emitting object.

For a long time, astronomers could only use their eyes to view celestial objects. They might peer through a telescope and see the brightness of the star and its relationship and position to other stars, but they couldn't record the light. They couldn't store it for future reference. They couldn't see very faint things because of the limited sensitivity of eyes.

Then, late in the 19th century, photographic emulsions were produced that allowed light to be stored for long periods of time, that allowed light to build up and show faint stars and produced a permanent record of their spatial positions relative to one another, and which could be studied for as long afterwards as needed. Astronomers no longer had to rely on memory.

This was a great advance in astronomy, but there were limitations. Photographic emulsions are not very sensitive. They detect and record only about 1% to 2% of incoming light. That's about how sensitive human eyes are. Our eyes don't really need to be much more sensitive than that because there's plenty of sunlight during the day with which we can see surrounding objects. Certainly, to see distant stars and galaxies, we have to have a more sensitive detector.

Another problem is that photographic emulsions are not really very linear. If you expose for a long time, you don't really make the star look brighter on the photograph. You reach a certain limiting value after which the emulsion doesn't really do you much good. So the size of a star or the apparent brightness of a star on a photographic emulsion is not really related to its true brightness in an easily defined, quantitative way.

In the late 1970s, CCDs were developed, charge-coupled devices, as shown here in a picture of my hand. These are little squares of silicon that are a semi-conducting substance. When the light hits them, the semi-conducting substance records an electric charge. What actually happens is that an electron shoots out of the position on the chip where the photon hit, and later you can measure the amount of charge that's missing from that position. That is directly related to the brightness of the star.

We can see in this schematic here a semi-conductor chip of this kind. There are typically 2,048 pixels, or picture elements, on a side. So, 2,048 times 2,048 are over four million. Modern CCDs have 4 million pixels on them. You can record the positions and brightness levels of stars over a fairly wide area with fairly good resolution using this chip.

Because the CCD uses the semi-conductor, it is enormously sensitive. It can detect 50% or 60%, up to 80%, of the incoming light. That's an enormous gain in sensitivity over the human eye. If you were detecting only 1% to 2% of the light with the eye or the photographic emulsion, and suddenly you detect 80% of the light, it is as though you had built a much bigger telescope capable of collecting more light. Here we did it much more cheaply, because we made use of the electronic revolution that produced these things. These CCDs are what you use in camcorder devices to produce images of your family, of mountains, and other things.

CCDs also offer the advantage of being highly linear. If you record a star that is four times as bright as another star intrinsically, it will appear four times as bright on a CCD. There is not this limiting factor beyond which the star stops looking brighter, as with a photographic emulsion. Moreover, the longer you expose on a CCD, the more charge builds up. Again, there isn't this limitation of photographic plates where you can only expose a certain length of time, then the plate fogs over.

They have a lot of good properties and they are used quite a lot these days. We even have mosaics of CCDs, where you might have one with 2,000 pixels on a side and another one with 2,000 pixels on a side—producing a square that's 8,000 pixels on a side—thereby increasing the area of the sky, which you can image. Now, these mosaics are being built even to the tune of four-by-four in a big square with 16 CCDs. That gives you a wider coverage of the sky over which you record the brightness levels of stars.

CCDs have revolutionized astronomy. They have made it possible to see extremely distant and faint objects in the universe, which would not have been possible to see with a photographic emulsion and certainly not possible to see with the eye.

The telescope is what gathers the light. Here is the Lick Observatory three-meter reflecting telescope. It has a mirror down here at the bottom, which gathers light. In this picture, the mirror is covered by a cap, which keeps dust, bird dung and other things from falling on it. The mirror is what gathers the light. The mirror of a telescope, like the three-meter mirror shown here, is a gigantic eyeball. It's like the pupil of your eye and it gathers all the light that rains down on it.

A distant star sends light out in all directions. Our pupils intercept only a tiny amount of light. A big telescope is like a big pupil. If it intercepts a larger amount of the incoming light, it will be able to see a fainter object because it's like a gigantic eye.

The telescope gathers the light and brings it to a focus on your photographic emulsion, CCD, or even your eye, if you're looking through an eyepiece. The amount of light that a telescope can gather per unit time is clearly proportional to the size of the telescope. By size I mean area, not the length of the tube. The length of the tube is actually immaterial for this discussion. It's the area of the telescope that tells you how much of this incoming light from a star you will be able to intercept. The larger the area, the greater the amount of light is gathered.

The radius of a circle is just its diameter divided by two, and the area of a circle is π times the radius squared (πr^2). That's just π times the diameter squared over four ($\pi D^2/4$).

So, if I have two telescopes of diameters D_1 and D_2, the ratio of their areas, A_2 divided by A_1, is simply equal to the ratio of the squares of the diameters, because the π's and 4's cancel out. The ratio of areas is simply the ratio of diameters squared.

Suppose we have a four-meter diameter mirror; that's fairly typical for telescopes in the 1990s. Our dilated pupil at night is only four millimeters in size. That's 0.001 of the size of a four-meter mirror. So the ratio of the diameters, four meters/0.004 meters, is 1,000 and you square the ratio of the diameters in order to get the ratio of areas. In this particular case, the ratio of areas of a four-meter telescope, and your four-millimeter eyeball is 1 million. It's $1,000^2$. If I were looking through a telescope 4 meters in diameter, I could see stars that are a million times fainter than the stars that I would see by eye, without the use of a telescope. It's that ratio of areas that effectively increases the light gathering ability and power of your eye, allowing you to see faint distant objects.

We want big telescopes. That's the name of the game in astronomy. We also want sensitive detectors, sensitive CCDs.

The other thing that a telescope does is to provide greater clarity of the images that we see. The angular measure of an object is just the apparent angular size in the sky. A full circle is 360° in the sky. If I go from horizon to horizon and then back down again and up, that full circle is 360°. Horizon to horizon is 180°. Horizon to zenith is 90°. One degree is divided into 60 minutes of arc, or arc minutes, denoted by '. Each degree is 60 arc minutes and a circle is 360°. Each arc minute is divided into 60 arc seconds, or 60 seconds of arc (denoted by ".). That's a very small unit. One arc second is roughly the angular size of a dime as seen from a distance of a few kilometers. It's a very small apparent size.

Notice that the angular size of an object decreases as the object's distance away from you increases. The physical size and the distance of an object dictate the apparent angular size of that object.

A telescope that provides great clarity is one that can separate stars that are away from each other in the sky by a small angular distance. If it blurs those stars together, then it doesn't have very good clarity. If it shows those stars as separate individual units, it has good clarity.

We want the clarity, or resolution, of the telescope to be sufficiently high that we can see objects that are at least one arc second apart from each other and, hopefully, even better than that, some 0.1 of an arc second apart or 0.01 of an arc second apart. The smaller the angular separation that you can resolve, the better off you are, because the more clarity you will be able to see in a distant galaxy.

Let's take a look at an example. Here in the left series of panels, in the left panel, you can see two stars through a blue filter. They barely touch each other. That is, with the naked eye, you can clearly see that there are two stars there, but they're barely touching each other. Through a telescope, the size of the blur circle of each star decreases. So, a telescope provides a clearer view of those two sizes because they are clearly separated from one another.

A bigger telescope makes the size of the blur circle even smaller. It doesn't increase the apparent separation between those two stars, because that's just the angular separation of the stars. That angular distance between the stars is the same through a big telescope as it is with your naked eye. But the size of the blur circle is smaller through a big telescope than with your eye. So, the clarity that you get is better with a telescope.

You can also see that redder wavelengths, longer wavelengths, are not resolved as clearly as bluer, shorter wavelengths are for a given sized telescope. Here is the view of two stars through a red filter using your naked eye. They appear kind of blurred together. Through a telescope, you can clearly resolve them, but not as clearly as was the case for blue light. Through an even larger telescope, they are more clearly resolved, but not quite as clearly as when viewed in blue light.

The angular resolution, or the angular size of the blur circle, is related to both the diameter of the telescope and the wavelength at which you are viewing the light. The angular size of the blur circle is proportional to the wavelength divided by the diameter of the mirror or lens of the telescope. If you increase the diameter, you get greater clarity and higher resolution. That's what was illustrated in that series of diagrams. Similarly, if you decrease the wavelength at which you're observing the object, you also decrease the angular size of the blur circle. For a given size telescope, you tend to see clearer images at blue wavelengths than at red wavelengths, because the blue wavelengths have a better, or higher, resolution and a smaller blur circle.

You might think this is great. Let's just make telescopes huge and they will improve the clarity with which we see the universe. The trouble is that our atmosphere blurs out the light from the stars. Beyond a diameter of 20 or 30 centimeters, a telescope theoretically improves the resolution with which you see stars; although in practice, it does not, because the blurring of the atmosphere becomes the dominant problem. Your telescope might have intrinsically better resolution, but the atmosphere is blurring it out anyway. It doesn't really do you much good in terms of clarity to produce bigger in size than 20 or 30 centimeters in diameter.

I'll have a caveat to that in a minute, but the main purpose of building big telescopes is to gather more light, not necessarily to improve the resolution.

Here is an example of a blurred image of an object. You can see five stars. These little dots are cosmic rays, charged particles that interacted with the CCD. You don't have to pay attention to them, but these five stars are definitely fuzzy looking. If you had better resolution, you could clearly separate them one from another, and you might see other, fainter stars that merge with the bright blurs of these bright stars.

One way of improving the resolution of telescopes on the ground is to remove the effects of the atmosphere by measuring what the atmosphere is doing and making the appropriate correction. If you have a bright star next to the object that you're trying to measure and you photograph that bright star many times per second, then, in fact, you can tell how much the atmosphere is blurring the star, first one way, then the other way. The atmosphere is moving around, so the rays of light are wiggling and jiggling. But if you measure the star many times per second, you can see what the atmosphere is doing and apply a correction that brings the star to a nice, sharp focus.

That correction, when applied to a nearby object close to that star, will make that object also appear nice and sharp. This process is called adaptive optics. Here you can see a simulation of what adaptive optics does for you using a telescope. Here is a picture of a galaxy with spiral arms using no adaptive optics corrections. Here are corrections using adaptive optics that are progressively better and better. You can see the arms more clearly as you improve the adaptive optics. You can even see individual stars and clusters of stars in the arms of this galaxy, whereas in the normal blurred atmospheric image, you could not see those individual stars and those clusters of stars.

This business of adaptive optics, in principle, improves our resolution tremendously, even with telescopes used on the ground. But this technology right now, in the middle 1990s is only still being developed. It should be finished, or quite workable, within a year or two. Already at Lick Observatory we have a laser beam shooting out of the three-meter telescope, which produces an artificial bright star next to the object you are studying. You can measure the apparent shape of that bright artificial star and make the appropriate corrections. Already, we can get images of other reasonably bright stars, close to your laser beam, that are pretty sharp. The technique is getting there, but we don't yet have beautiful pictures of entire galaxies like those that I will later show you from the Hubble Space Telescope. The technology is being developed. It's already shown pairs of stars that merged together when normally viewed from the ground as individual separate stars. That's of interest, but I would say the technology is not quite there yet to show individual galaxies with stars and clusters within those galaxies. Within a few years we will be there. So, this procedure of adaptive optics is one way to get around the problem of the Earth's atmosphere.

Let's discuss how a telescope actually forms an image. The first type of telescope that I'll discuss is the refracting telescope, which consists of a lens. A lens can bring the incoming light into focus. It collects the light and brings it to focus one focal length away from the lens. Such a telescope collects parallel beams of light from distant stars. Why do I say they are parallel? In this diagram, you can see that a nearby object has light rays that diverge, and observers on different parts of the Earth will see that star as being in different directions. The light is approaching an observer here at the North Pole of the Earth from one direction, while an observer from the South Pole sees the light coming from another direction, and the light rays are clear diverge.

The more distant a star is, the less the rays appear to diverge as seen from the Earth. Here from this quite distant star, we can see that the opening angle, the angle of apparent divergence, is less than it was for a nearby star.

Stars are effectively so far away that the opening angle is very small by the time the light reaches the Earth. Light rays appear as though they are coming in along parallel paths. This is true even for light that is coming from an object as nearby as the Sun, 150 million kilometers away. The light rays from the Sun are essentially parallel when they reach us. From stars, which are even farther away from the Sun, the light rays are truly parallel when they reach us. That's why I showed parallel light rays when I showed that lens collecting the light.

One of the earliest so-called refracting telescopes was that of Galileo. In 1609, he probably heard about the idea that was developed by Dutch opticians, but he made his own telescopes, two of which are shown here. They were very simple primitive things. There was just a lens at one end of the tube and an eyepiece at the other end. By looking through the eyepiece like this, the light from a distant star comes through the lens; the lens collects a lot of light, and brings it to focus somewhere inside the tube. Then the eyepiece lens helps the eye form an image of the object that you're absorbing.

This simple little telescope consists of a lens that collects the light and a lens at the eyepiece end that helps form an image on your eye. He did this in 1609-1610 and made some tremendous discoveries, as I'll discuss later.

Each individual monocular in a pair of binoculars is also a refracting telescope. We call them refracting telescopes because the lens bends the light to a focus. These are very simple to build but quite effective. Unfortunately, they have a problem. As you can see here, the lens brings different colors of light to different foci. The violet light gets brought to a closer focus than the red light. The green light is in between. This effect, called chromatic aberration, means that if you put a photographic emulsion at one position—say, at the position of the green focus—you're allowing light of all wavelengths to come in through the lens, but not all wavelengths will appear to be in focus. The overall image of the object, the star, will be out of focus. Although the green light will be in focus, the violet, blue and red lights will be out of focus. This chromatic aberration is a limitation of the refracting telescope.

Another limitation is that a lens cannot be supported from the bottom. The light has to go through the lens in order to be seen on the other end, so you have to support the lens at the periphery of the lens, and that tends to make the lens sag. There are other problems with refractors, so the biggest refractors in the world are only about a meter in diameter.

Here's the Lick Observatory 36-inch refractor. It has an enormous length. The focal length of the lens is huge compared to a person, seen down here, but the diameter is only about 36 inches. This is the second largest refractor in the world. The biggest one is not much bigger. It's only 30 inches across and it's at the Yerkes Observatory in Wisconsin.

The Lick refractor was built in 1888. Lick Observatory was the first observatory on a remote mountain site. That was considered to be a rather foreign concept at the time, when telescopes were built, mostly at university campuses, which were in cities. James Lick, a wealthy San Francisco merchant, donated a lot of money for the construction of this telescope. He actually wanted a monument to himself. He wanted to build a pyramid in downtown San Francisco that would contain his body, but his friends convinced him that lots of civilizations had built pyramids in the past, that he would not be doing anything really new by building a pyramid, so why not instead donate his money to something useful. He allowed his money to be used to build what was then the largest telescope in the world, a 36-inch refractor at the most remote site known, the best site in the world, near San Jose. California. That's why the Lick Observatory is there.

He requested that his body be placed at the base of the telescope. He actually died before the telescope was completed, but after completion, his body was indeed placed below the base of the telescope, and there lies the body of James Lick. He actually debated whether he wanted to be cremated or not. His colleagues suggested he be cremated, but after some thought he said, "Certainly not, I intend to rot like a gentleman." Before they put his body below the base of the 36-inch refractor, they opened the coffin to make sure that no grave robbers had stolen the body and saw that Lick's wish had been fulfilled. He had indeed rotted like a gentleman.

Now let me discuss reflecting telescopes. Reflecting telescopes operate on a different principle. Instead of having a lens gathering the light, they have a mirror at the bottom gathering the light and bringing it to a focus. The focus can be within the tube as shown here; that's called the prime focus. Clearly, that doesn't work very well for a small telescope because if your head or your eyeball were at the prime focus, then your head would block the incoming light. For example, if this was a reflecting telescope and the mirror was at the bottom, and I stuck my head here at the prime focus, my head would block the incoming light.

Newton realized this and built a different type of telescope. In fact, he invented the reflecting telescope, and the kind he invented was like this. The light comes in, hits the mirror, bounces off and then hits a secondary mirror, which deflects the light through a hole in the side of the tube of the telescope. You might think that the secondary mirror would produce a hole in the object you're viewing, for example, a hole in Jupiter. But it doesn't do that because every little part of the mirror forms a complete image of the object. You get a complete image of Jupiter from every part of the mirror. The hole where the secondary mirror blocks of some of the light simply decreases the apparent brightness of Jupiter. It doesn't produce a hole in Jupiter; it just decreases the number of photons hitting the primary mirror, so it makes Jupiter appear less bright.

Another technique is to bounce the light off the secondary mirror and, through a hole in the primary mirror; the light can then be collected at the bottom here. You can attach a permanent instrument more easily on the bottom than you can on the side of the tube.

Modern instruments weigh many tons and, if you put them on the side of the tube, it would make the telescope quite imbalanced. Moreover, the balance would change with the orientation of the telescope in the sky. This so-called Cassegrain focus is what's almost exclusively used these days, as opposed to the Newtonian focus and the prime focus.

The shape of the mirror is very important. The easiest shape to grind is that of the surface of a sphere. That's easy to grind. Unfortunately, a spherical surface does not bring parallel incoming rays to a common focus. Light waves farther from the axis, or center, of the sphere get brought to a focus closer in to the mirror than light waves coming in closer to the center of the mirror. This is an effect called spherical aberration. The simplest kind of mirror to grind suffers from spherical aberration. As I'll discuss in the next lecture, the Hubble Space Telescope initially suffered from a little bit of spherical aberration; it had the wrong global shape to its mirror.

To correct this, what we actually want to do is produce a parabolic or, in some cases, a hyperbolic shape. This is just a different sort of a curve. It's slightly more open than a sphere. If you take a sphere and open it up a little bit, you produce a parabola or a hyperbola. That brings those rays to a common focus. That's just a little bit of a technical difficulty, but it's no huge deal.

A parabolic shape limits the field of view over which you get good sharp images. The primary limitation of a parabolic focus is unlimited field of view. You can correct for that by having a spherical mirror down at one end and then a corrector plate at the top end. The corrector plate can produce an effect opposite to the bad effect that a spherical mirror produces. The net effect is to make light come to a common focus.

What's really great about a Schmidt telescope, which is this particular design, is that light coming in from a wide variety of angles—that is, over a wide region of the sky—gets brought to the correct focus. Schmidt telescopes have particularly wide fields of view. At Palomar Observatory in southern California, there is a very large Schmidt telescope that was used to make a map of the sky, roughly 1,000 overlapping photographs. Each of those photographs was about six degrees on a side. That's a very wide field and big angular size. Normal parabolic mirrors without the Schmidt design have much smaller fields of view, maybe only a few arc minutes. This is good if you want to use wide angles.

For a long time, the Palomar 200-inch, or five-meter, telescope was the largest one in existence. It was completed in 1948, and for about forty years it was the biggest one. Why? It was the biggest because it was cheaper to improve detectors than to build bigger telescopes. Big telescopes are expensive. In general, the cost of an object grows in proportion to the mass of the stuff within it. You've got more things to support, bigger gears, and all that kind of stuff. So, big telescopes are really expensive to build.

But, from 1948 to the mid-1980s, we witnessed the electronic revolution. A whole series of progressively better detectors were constructed culminating with the CCDs, the charge-coupled devices, which were perfected in the early 1980s, and now are really very good and very big. For many decades, there was no real reason to build better telescopes. You could just build better detectors; that was much cheaper than building bigger telescopes. By the time you detect 50% or 80% of the light, you can't do any better. CCDs are about as good as they get in terms of efficiency and in terms of detecting the amount of incident light. In order to gain more light, we have to build bigger telescopes. Now that we have detectors that are about as good as they are going to be, we have to build bigger telescopes.

Look at the three-meter reflecting mirror in the telescope at Lick Observatory. It is very thick. It has to be that thick in order to prevent it from warping under its sheer weight. You might think that by making it thicker, you make its weight bigger, but it turns out that you increase the stiffness. You gain stability overall if you make the mirror thicker, but you then have to support this gargantuan mirror. It's hard to grind the mirror; it takes a long time to grind it and for the mirror to cool down. It's a real problem; it's hard to build bigger mirrors.

We found a way to do it. Here is the design of the Keck telescopes on Mauna Kea volcano in Hawaii. Instead of having one monolithic ten-meter mirror in diameter, there are 36 segments, each of which is only about 1.5 meters from one distant corner to the other (about 0.9 meters from edge to edge). These mirrors arranged in a honeycomb pattern, like this, and they can be used then to simulate a monolithic ten-meter diameter mirror. You can actually change the orientation of each segment individually in order to have it conform to the desired shape of a single monolithic mirror. But each segment is much smaller; hence, much thinner, easier to support, and cheaper to build than a large monolithic mirror.

Here is the size of one of these mirrors compared with a person. You can see they are nearly the size of a person. In the next slide, you can see an aerial view of the Keck telescope with the mirrors in their honeycomb pattern. In the middle there is a person, so you can see roughly what the size of each segment is. It's a tiny bit smaller than a person.

The Keck telescopes—now there are two of them—are wonderful devices. They are the biggest telescopes in the world right now, in the middle of 1998, at least for optical work. They produce stunningly beautiful views of the distant parts of the universe. We like to work up on this high mountain in Hawaii because you can play in the snow if you like, although it's hard to think at 14,000 feet. Then later in the day, if you have time, you can go down to the beach, so, you can ski and go to the beach on the same day if you want. Of course, usually we're so tired and busy observing that we don't have time to do any of these things. This was before the observing run started.

Another way to do it is actually to build a monolithic mirror and make it thin. Maybe it won't support itself the right way, but if you have active little gizmos behind the mirror you can change the orientation of different parts of this thin mirror as though it were built out of different segments. You don't actually need there to be separate segments. You just need little things underneath the glass to maintain the proper shape. Some observatories, instead of making segmented mirrors, are building single thin monolithic mirrors, which have these little gizmos on the back that constantly maintain the correct shape of the mirror. That's another way to go.

Also, you can make a thin mirror, but make it structurally very stable by having a honeycomb structure of glass behind it. Most of the space is empty but the honeycomb structure behind the glass provides great stability. It's sort of like the Keck design but with a monolithic mirror, with the honeycomb providing stability behind the mirror. That's another way of increasing the size of the telescope without increase its weight very much.

114

Let's go back to this angular size of the blur circle. Recall that it's proportional to the wavelength that you're viewing and the diameter of the lens or mirror. For a given wavelength, to improve the clarity, you want to increase the diameter, assuming you have something like adaptive optics to improve the resolution and optical wavelengths.

At radio wavelengths, λ is very large. λ for radio wavelengths can be meters or tens of meters or kilometers in size. If you've used a puny little telescope only a meter or even ten meters in size, and the wave is one kilometer in size, you're going to get terrible clarity. You're going to get a giant blur circle. At optical wavelengths, we're using mirrors that are a meter in size, but what's the wavelength of optical light? It's tiny. You can't even picture what it is. I talked about how big it is a few lectures ago. So, λ/D for optical light is small, hence the clarity is really good, but λ/D for radio waves, the clarity is very poor.

What can we do? Can we build a radio telescope the size of California or New York or something? Clearly that would be impossible. It would be prohibitively expensive, and it would blot out the sun for a lot of people.

You build the radio dishes as big as you can. Here is a many tens-of-meters-sized dish in the Owens Valley in California. This telescope, is owned by Cal Tech, provides reasonably good resolution, but to get really good resolution, you want an even bigger mirror. The Arecibo Radio Telescope in Puerto Rico is about 1,000 feet in diameter. It's really huge compared to even the Keck telescopes.

But there is something we can do even better. We can actually place the telescopes apart from one another like this, two telescopes separated from one another. Although they won't have the light gathering ability of a single giant telescope of that size, they have the clarity or resolution of a telescope whose diameter is equal to the spacing between these two telescopes. In terms of clarity, by linking these two telescopes together, one gets just as good a result as if one had a single gigantic telescope the size of California or the United States or whatever. You don't get as much light gathering ability. You don't collect as much light as with a giant mirror, but you get the clarity and you do it for a reasonable cost. You essentially use the interference of light that I discussed two lectures ago to improve the clarity obtained with these two telescopes.

Here is a picture of the Very Large Array in New Mexico, an array of 27 radio telescopes whose clarity is equivalent to that of a single telescope of a diameter equal to the very most extended legs of the array. This was much cheaper to build than a gigantic telescope. Even at optical wavelengths and infrared wavelengths, we are trying to develop the technology to do this. This technique is called interferometry. It works most easily at radio wavelengths, because radio wavelengths are long and not much affected by Earth's atmosphere. Optical wavelengths are affected a lot, but we're working on the technology to allow us to link interferometrically the two Keck telescopes, which are separated by about 85 meters, in order to produce a supremely clear image at optical wavelengths. We can do it already at radio wavelengths because the radio wavelengths are easier to deal with, but soon we hope to be able to do this at optical wavelengths. NASA is funding a very large project of this sort with the Keck telescopes because NASA is interested in seeing pictures of planets around other stars. You can't do that at optical wavelengths, even with the Hubble Space Telescope, because the resolution isn't good enough. We need, effectively, a gargantuan telescope. Stay tuned; this is something we expect to see great improvement on in the near future.

Lecture Six
Space Telescopes and the Celestial Sphere

Scope:

Telescopes in space are unaffected by atmospheric turbulence, have very dark skies, and can probe previously unobservable regions of the electromagnetic spectrum. NASA's Hubble Space Telescope has played an especially prominent role in the 1990s, providing superb data at optical, ultraviolet, and infrared wavelengths. We then introduce the celestial sphere, in which the stars and planets appear to be embedded. Generally, the stars of a given constellation are not physically associated with each other, but simply form a pattern in the sky. The celestial sphere appears to rotate around us as Earth spins about its axis; the specific constellations that are visible depend on one's location on Earth's surface, the time of night, and the time of year. Contrary to popular belief, the seasons are a consequence of the tilt of Earth's rotation axis relative to the axis of Earth's orbital plane.

Objectives

Upon completion of this lecture, you should be able to:

1. Explain why some telescopes are placed above the Earth's atmosphere, despite the higher cost than that of ground-based telescopes.

2. Describe the problem suffered by the Hubble Space Telescope during its first few years of operation.

3. Define various terms associated with the celestial sphere, such as the celestial poles, celestial equator, horizon, zenith, and meridian.

4. Summarize what an observer viewing the celestial sphere would see from different locations on Earth and at different times of the night.

5. Explain why the constellations visible in the evening sky gradually change over the course of a year.

6. Discuss the reason for the seasons on Earth.

Outline

I. Telescopes in space play a prominent role in astronomy.

    A. Observations from the ground, especially at low altitudes, have some disadvantages.

        1. The Earth's atmosphere distorts (blurs) the images.

        2. Scattered light from cities and the Moon brightens the sky.

        3. The sky glows naturally; it is especially bright at infrared wavelengths.

        4. The atmosphere is opaque to many regions of the electromagnetic spectrum.

            a. Ozone (O_3) at altitudes of 20-40 km blocks UV radiation.

            b. Water vapor (H_2O) at altitudes of 2-10 km blocks some infrared wavelengths.

            c. Various atoms and molecules block x-rays and gamma rays.

    B. Telescopes on high, dry mountains far from city lights alleviate some of these problems. A good example is Mauna Kea volcano in Hawaii, at an altitude of about 4 km.

        1. Atmospheric blurring is less, but still significant.

        2. The sky is darker, but there remains some scattered starlight and natural glow.

        3. Parts of the infrared spectrum are available, but most is not.

        4. X-rays, gamma rays, and the UV are still blocked.

    C. Since space telescopes are expensive, they should be reserved only for those observations that cannot be obtained in other ways.

        1. Some parts of the infrared can be studied with telescopes in airplanes, but others require a space telescope.

        2. X-rays and gamma rays from bright objects can be studied with instruments carried by high-altitude balloons, or launched on short trips by rockets. Orbiting satellites provide more stability and longer duration for observations of faint objects.

        3. For UV wavelengths, orbiting space telescopes are used. A good example is the International Ultraviolet

Explorer, which provided UV spectra of objects for nearly two decades before it was terminated in 1996.

D. NASA's Hubble Space Telescope (HST), with a 2.4-m primary mirror, has been enormously important: it provides very sharp images at UV, optical, and IR wavelengths, and it is also able to obtain spectra.

1. The telescope was in the planning and construction stages for nearly two decades.

2. The Space Shuttle *Challenger* disaster in 1986 was a major setback.

3. An error in the polishing of the primary mirror resulted in some spherical aberration, discovered only after launch in April 1990.

4. Computer processing of the data made it possible to achieve the desired angular resolution in images of bright objects, but faint objects could not be seen.

5. The projects to be done with HST were re-prioritized: those least affected by the problem were done first.

6. In December 1993, astronauts aboard the Space Shuttle completed a highly successful repair mission: the main imaging camera was replaced, and corrective optics were inserted for the other instruments. (These are analogous to glasses or contact lenses, but with mirrors.) Several other items were also fixed or replaced.

7. The resulting data from HST are spectacular, and will be shown throughout this course.

8. In February 1997, Space Shuttle astronauts visited HST again to replace some damaged parts and to install a near-infrared camera.

E. NASA is now planning a Next Generation Space Telescope. The preliminary design in 1998 has an 8-m mirror, with hardware optimized for infrared observations.

II. Let us now consider the celestial sphere.

A. Ancient astronomers in Egypt and elsewhere grouped the visible stars into constellations.

1. These were given names, occasionally because they resembled something (e.g., Scorpius, the Scorpion), but mostly to honor the object.

2. Easily recognized patterns of stars that do not constitute a constellation are called asterisms. The most familiar

example is the Big Dipper, which is part of the constellation Ursa Major (the Great Bear).

3. Most of the names and legends we now associate with constellations are from Greek mythology, but some of the ones visible only from the Earth's Southern Hemisphere have more modern origins (e.g., "Telescopium").

4. Astronomers now officially recognize 88 constellations, and each point in the sky is assigned to only one of them.

5. The stars in most constellations and asterisms are at different distances from Earth, and are not physically associated with each other, but simply appear along nearly the same line of sight.

   a. The Big Dipper is somewhat of an exception to this: five of its seven stars probably formed together, and are moving through space in roughly the same direction.

   b. Nevertheless, even these stars now have different distances from us, and in any case the other two stars are not at all associated, and are more distant.

6. The apparent shapes of constellations and asterisms change slowly with time, as the stars move relative to each other.

   a. The handle of the Big Dipper, for example, was slightly straighter 50,000 years ago, and will be significantly more bent 50,000 years from now.

   b. Note that these changes are produced by motion *across* the sky (i.e., perpendicular to the line of sight). The radial motions of stars (i.e., along our line of sight, and measurable with the Doppler effect) do not contribute.

B. Stars appear to be fixed to a very large celestial sphere that rotates around us.

   1. This is a consequence of the enormous distances of stars.

      a. We have no depth perception, because the stars are so far away.

      b. Regardless of one's place on Earth, a given star appears along the same absolute direction in space, since its light rays are essentially parallel.

2. When standing at a given location, the zenith is defined to be the point straight overhead, and the horizon is 90° away in all directions, along lines tangent to the smooth surface (ignore irregularities like mountains and valleys).

3. The north and south celestial poles are the extensions of the Earth's axis of rotation to the celestial sphere.

4. The celestial equator is the projection of Earth's equator onto the celestial sphere. It is a "great circle"—that is, a circle formed by the intersection of a sphere and a plane that passes through the center of the sphere.

5. The meridian is the great circle through the celestial poles and the zenith. When a star reaches its highest position in the sky, it is crossing the meridian.

6. Each object in the celestial sphere can be assigned coordinates analogous to longitude and latitude on Earth. These are called "right ascension" and "declination," respectively.

7. From any point on Earth that has a clear horizon, one can see only half of the celestial sphere at any given time. This can be visualized by extending a plane tangent to the surface so that it intersects the very distant celestial sphere.

C. The rotation of the celestial sphere is a consequence of the Earth's rotation about its own axis: as Earth rotates in one direction, the stars move across the sky in the opposite direction.

1. Stars move in circles centered on the north and south celestial poles.

2. If one is standing at the Earth's north or South Poles, stars move in circles parallel to the horizon; the altitude of a star never changes.

    a. All of the visible stars are "circumpolar"—they are always above the horizon.

    b. Only half of the entire celestial sphere (either the northern or Southern Hemisphere) is observable over the course of a 24-hour day (or even a year).

3. If one is standing at the Earth's equator, stars rise straight up, cross the sky, and set straight down; the altitude of a given star changes with time.

    a. No stars are circumpolar.

         b. Although at any given time one can see only half of the celestial sphere, over a 24-hour day all parts of the celestial sphere rise above the horizon.

   4. If one is standing at intermediate latitudes, stars rise and set at an angle.

         a. Stars sufficiently close to the celestial pole are circumpolar.

         b. More than half of the celestial sphere is observable over a 24-hour day.

   5. Stunning photographs of the motions of stars can be easily made by putting a single-lens reflex camera on a tripod, aiming at one part of the sky, and opening the shutter for an extended period of time (say, a few minutes to a few hours). Be sure to turn of the flash!

D. Polaris, the "North Star," is nearly at the location of the north celestial pole.

   1. However, this will not always be the case. Owing to the gravitational influence of the Moon and Sun, the Earth's axis of rotation slowly changes orientation, tracing a full circle in the sky (of radius 23.5°) over the course of 26,000 years.

   2. Currently there is no bright star near the south celestial pole.

E. Our view of the night sky changes over the course of a year.

   1. In December, the constellation Orion crosses the meridian at midnight.

   2. Three months later, in March, when the Earth has moved through one quarter of its orbit around the Sun, the constellation Virgo crosses the meridian at midnight, when Orion is setting. Orion crosses the meridian at sunset (i.e., 6 hours earlier than in December).

   3. Thus, each successive night, Orion crosses the meridian about 4 minutes earlier: 3 months is about 90 days, and (4 minutes/day)(90 days) = 360 minutes = 6 hours.

   4. Three months later, in June, Orion crosses the meridian another 6 hours earlier—i.e., at noon. Hence, it isn't visible at night. Instead, the constellation Ophiuchus crosses the meridian at midnight.

5. Thus, a given star rises (and crosses the meridian) 4 minutes earlier each day, and our overall view of the celestial sphere gradually changes during the year.

6. Microscopically, what happens is that the Earth travels roughly 1° along its orbit each day. The changing perspective causes the "solar day" (the time interval been two consecutive meridian crossings of the Sun) to be about 4 minutes longer than the "sidereal day" (the time interval between two consecutive meridian crossings of a given star). The actual difference is 3 minutes and 56 seconds.

7. As seen from Earth, the yearly path that the Sun follows among the stars (due to Earth's orbital motion) is called the ecliptic. It is the great circle formed by the intersection of Earth's orbital plane and the celestial sphere.

III. The seasons manifest themselves primarily as changes in the length of time the Sun is above the horizon each day, and also in the average daily temperatures.

A. In the discussion below, we neglect the fact that the top of the Sun rises slightly before the middle, and that the bending of light by Earth's atmosphere makes the Sun visible even when it is slightly below the horizon. Both of these effects increase the length of daytime over nighttime.

B. Contrary to popular belief, the seasons are *not* caused by changes in the distance between the Earth and the Sun.
1. The seasons would not be opposite in the northern and Southern Hemispheres.
2. Changes in the Earth-Sun distance would also not affect the duration of daytime hours.
3. Northern Hemisphere summer actually occurs when the Earth is farthest from the Sun.

C. The seasons are a consequence of the tilt of Earth's axis of rotation (23.5°) relative to the axis of Earth's orbital plane.
1. The axis of rotation points along an essentially fixed absolute direction in space. (As mentioned above, it varies only over thousands of years, due to the gravitational pull of the Moon and Sun.) However, it changes direction relative to the *Sun* as the Earth orbits over the course of a year.

2. When the Earth's North Pole is tilted in the general direction of the Sun, as in Northern Hemisphere spring and summer, the Sun stays above the horizon for more than 12 hours in the Northern Hemisphere and for less than 12 hours in the Southern Hemisphere.

   a. Daytime grows progressively longer at higher northern latitudes, and as the date approaches June 22 (when the tilt toward the Sun is aligned best).

   b. With longer days, the heating of the water, ground, and atmosphere grows.

   c. Also, the Sun passes closer to the zenith, so the sunlight is more direct: a given beam of light intercepts a smaller area than it does when the light strikes at a glancing angle, so the heating per unit area is greater.

   d. Note that this increase in the heating rate is *not* due to the closer *distance* between the Northern Hemisphere and the Sun at this time; the difference in distance is very minor.

3. Six months later, when the Earth's North Pole is tilted in the general direction opposite the Sun, as in Northern Hemisphere fall and winter, the Sun stays above the horizon for less than 12 hours in the Northern Hemisphere and for more than 12 hours in the Southern Hemisphere.

4. Regions near the poles experience the largest changes with the seasons.

   a. The "midnight sun" can be seen on at least one day anywhere north of latitude 66.5° or south of latitude −66.5°.

   b. At the poles there are 6 continuous months of daytime followed by 6 continuous months of nighttime.

D. The starting times of the seasons in the Northern Hemisphere are as follows. (Seasons in the Southern Hemisphere are reversed from this.)

   1. The first day of summer is around June 22 (the "summer solstice"), when the Earth's North Pole most directly points toward the Sun. Thereafter, the Northern Hemisphere tilts progressively less toward the Sun.

2. The first day of fall is around September 22 (the "autumnal equinox"), when neither hemisphere is tilted toward the Sun. Thereafter, the Southern Hemisphere tilts progressively more toward the Sun.

3. The first day of winter is around December 22 (the "winter solstice"), when the Earth's South Pole most directly points toward the Sun. Thereafter, the Southern Hemisphere tilts progressively less toward the Sun.

4. The first day of spring is around March 22 (the "vernal equinox"), when neither hemisphere is tilted toward the Sun. Thereafter, the Northern Hemisphere tilts progressively more toward the Sun.

E. Although the 3-month interval during which the Sun is highest in the sky (in the Northern Hemisphere) is roughly May 7 through August 7, the highest temperatures generally occur in July through September; the lag occurs because it takes time for the oceans and land masses to heat up.

Essential Reading:

Chaisson, E. *The Hubble Wars.* HarperCollins, 1994.

Pasachoff, J. M. *Peterson's First Guide to Astronomy.* Houghton Mifflin, 1997.

Petersen, C. C., and Brandt, J. C. *Hubble Vision: Astronomy with the Hubble Space Telescope.* Cambridge Univ. Press, 1995.

Rey, H. *The Stars: A New Way to See Them.* Houghton Mifflin, 1976.

Questions to Consider:

1. Was the Hubble Space Telescope worth the roughly $2 billion that it cost? Reconsider this question after finishing the video course.

2. At Earth's poles, why does the Sun (or part of the Sun) actually appear above the horizon for somewhat *more* than 6 continuous months, rather than exactly 6 continuous months?

3. What would the seasons be like if (a) Earth's axis of rotation were parallel to the axis of Earth's orbital plane, and (b) the axis of rotation were in the orbital plane?

Lecture Six—Transcript
Space Telescopes and the Celestial Sphere

As we saw last time, telescopes play a crucial role in astronomy. We use them to collect light, bring it to a focus, and then analyze the light. The telescopes on the ground have a number of disadvantages. The first, as we have seen already and is shown again in this image, is that the stars are blurred by the Earth's atmosphere. Although there are techniques that are beginning to overcome that, such as adaptive optics and interferometry, there are limitations to those techniques and it will probably be a while before we get wide-angle images of the sky that are perfectly crisp and clear from the ground. So, blurring is a problem.

Another problem is that the sky is bright at night especially near cities, such as San Jose, as seen here from Lick Observatory. We can get far away from cities, and that helps us to some degree, but the sky also glows naturally at night. It's not perfectly black out there. There are molecules and things jumping around from one energy level to another, emitting light. This is especially the case at infrared wavelengths. At infrared wavelengths, our atmosphere glows to quite a considerable degree. At some infrared wavelengths, the sky is just as bright at night as it is during the day. We can't get away from the brightness of the night sky down here on Earth.

The third is that, as we've seen, electromagnetic radiation consists not just of visible light, but also at wavelengths shorter than violet, such as ultraviolet, X rays and *gamma* rays, and wavelengths longer than red, like the infrared and radio. Visible light and radio waves are transmitted by the Earth's atmosphere and some infrared waves are as well, but ultraviolet photons are blocked by ozone in the Earth's atmosphere at altitudes of 20-40 kilometers above the Earth's surface. Infrared is blocked by water vapor roughly two to ten kilometers above the Earth's surface. X rays and *gamma* rays are blocked by a variety of molecules in the Earth's atmosphere.

The only things that come through well are visible light, radio waves and a little bit of infrared. We would like to study the entire electromagnetic spectrum, and we can't do that from the ground simply because the light is blocked.

We can overcome some of these difficulties by going to high mountain sites, such as this one, Mauna Kea volcano in Hawaii. I mentioned it last time because I said the twin Keck telescopes, run by Cal Tech and the University of California with some support from NASA and Hawaii, are up there. You can see them here in this image, right there and there. There are about a dozen other telescopes way up there on this high forlorn peak. It's way far away from major city lights, so it's a pretty dark sky, although we can't get away from the natural sky glow. It's pretty high up as well, so we get above some, but not all, of the water vapor that messes up infrared wavelengths, for example. It's a good site, but it doesn't overcome all the difficulties. There's even a little bit of blurring there because, although we're above much of the atmosphere, we're not above the remaining parts and they still cause the stars to blur.

We can put some telescopes in airplanes. This is an artist's conception of what an infrared telescope to be completed within the next few years will look like. It will fly in an airplane and there will be a little window in the airplane through which the telescope looks. This is based on a previous design that was very successful. It was called the Kuiper Airborne Observatory and it has provided many good infrared views of the heavens. This telescope, SOPHIA, will be even better.

In general, it's cheap to keep telescopes on the ground and to fly them in airplanes. It's expensive to send telescopes way up in space in permanent Earth orbit. When possible, we should do projects with ground-based telescopes or with telescopes flown in airplanes, because per bit of information, the observations are cheaper. Astronomy has limited funding.

But there are some observations that can only be done with space telescopes, so we need to launch them. This is an example of an infrared telescope, IRAS, that was flown in the early 1980s. It produced some stunning information about the sky at infrared wavelengths that are simply not visible from the ground because our sky is so bright due to the glowing Earth's atmosphere. IRAS did a very good job.

There was an ultraviolet telescope called the International Ultraviolet Explorer that provided data at UV wavelengths for nearly twenty years before it was decommissioned a couple of years ago.

We've done pretty well in terms of space telescopes and used them wisely, and fairly cheaply. What we really wanted to do was have a permanent space telescope with a large mirror orbiting the Earth providing nice images. Most of these other telescopes didn't provide nice images. The Hubble Space Telescope was designed for that purpose and was launched with the Space Shuttle in April of 1990. It had a 2.4-meter diameter mirror. It would provide nice images because it had a whole set of CCDs built inside, and it would really improve the clarity with which we could view the Universe by roughly a factor of ten over what had been achievable prior to that time.

Suppose you have 20/200 vision. It's as though you suddenly put on a pair of glasses or contact lenses that improved your vision to 20/20. That's the kind of improvement in clarity at optical wavelengths that we expected with the Hubble Space Telescope, the first real large telescope to have good imaging devices within it.

Here is an artist's view of what the Hubble Space Telescope would look like viewing a galaxy far away. Above the Earth's atmosphere, it would not only have a clear view of that galaxy, but it could also observe at ultraviolet wavelengths and infrared wavelengths. It's really not designed to view the Universe at *gamma* ray, X ray or radio wavelengths.

We expected these very clear images, but here's what we have. Most of the light is spread out in a very awful looking pattern, like this. Only a small percentage of the light is focused sharply in the center, as it should have been if the space telescope had been properly manufactured. Most of the light should have been in the center.

This was a disaster. What went wrong? The mirror of the telescope shown here has slightly the wrong shape globally. It is a nice, perfectly smooth surface. If you measured the irregularities on it and expanded the mirror to the size of the United States, they would be only about six inches high. If you did the same thing to your glasses, the irregularities would be the size of skyscrapers.

So, the smoothness was not a problem, but the global shape was a problem. It suffered from spherical aberration. The mirror was a little bit too much like the shape of the surface of a sphere. It wasn't exactly the right shape. This was a problem that had been partly noticed when the mirror was still on the ground, but two tests had been done. One indicated that something was wrong; the other indicated that everything was okay. The people on the ground decided to trust the test that said that everything was okay. That was, I think, a case of being "penny wise and pound foolish". It would not have been too difficult or expensive to have a third test prior to launch or, better yet, to have figured out what was wrong with the telescope.

There were enormous headlines after this. *Newsweek* ran one that said "Star-crossed: NASA's $1.5 Billion Blunder". Another story said "Heaven Can Wait". There were all sorts of cartoons, such as pictures of God saying, "No pictures, please." It was not a good public relations event for science or astronomy.

Admittedly, the mistake should not have been made. But was all hope lost? Not really. Here is a picture of a star cluster taken from the ground. Don't worry too much about the square shape of the stars. That's just an artifact of the pixels on the CCD that was used to take the picture. What you should look at is that there is a bunch of stars that are spaced quite closely together, and it's hard to tell one star apart from the other.

Here, in the next image, is the same cluster imaged with the Hubble Space Telescope, with its limitations. However, what was done to this image was some computer processing. Since, after the fact, we knew exactly what the problem was, we could correct the light that was detected and make it look like the images were sharp. This technique works quite well, as long as the stars are sufficiently bright to have registered enough light in that small sharp core that only had a minor fraction of the total light. If your star was too faint to have registered enough light in that core, then this reconstruction didn't work very well. But if your star was bright enough to register enough light in the sharp core, you could run these computer reconstruction techniques and gain back what you lost.

What happened was that for the first couple of years of the Hubble Space Telescope, the projects that were to be done over its 10- or 15-year lifetime were simply reprioritized. Those that were least affected by the spherical aberration were done first, saving the harder projects for later on when the telescope got fixed. We actually used the telescope wisely during the time when it was still in its original form.

Nevertheless, we wanted it to be fixed once and for all, and here in this slide you can see a picture of the astronauts during the December 1993 servicing mission where they effectively placed corrective optics into the telescope. In one case, they completely replaced one of the cameras of the telescope. In some of the other instruments, they essentially put the equivalent of contact lenses, but in this case it's all done with mirrors because you don't want chromatic aberration.

They put these little corrective optics into the telescope to produce a sharp focus. They were absolute heroes. They did that, and they fixed some other broken things and replaced the solar panels that were about to break off; they did a lot of things. In this slide, you can see a before and after comparison of the center part of a galaxy. Before correction for the optics, or for the spherical aberration, and afterwards, you can see the great difference in the clarity of the image.

Another example is this famous picture, the Hubble Deep Field, where you can see in the small tiny part of the sky, one-one-hundredth million of the total sky, you can actually see 1,000 galaxies. Almost all of these little dots are galaxies like our Milky Way. Only one or two of the dots is a star in our own galaxy. A picture like this couldn't have been obtained from the ground. This is the kind of clarity that can only be achieved with a telescope in space, at least based on the kind of technology that we have right now and for the foreseeable future, the next ten to twenty years.

Here is a picture of a dying star. We'll study these later. It's a Sun-like star that's burping out its outer atmosphere of gas in its dying stages. It's sort of erupting in a gentle way, spewing this stuff out. We can now study the details of this process with the refurbished Hubble Space Telescope.

Here is another famous picture of the Eagle nebula. It is a bunch of gas and dust that is so dense that you can't see through it. That's why it appears dark. It is in these densest parts that gas and dust are gravitationally contracting right as we speak to form new stars. New stars are being formed inside those pillars. We can actually see those stars in the process of formation by using infrared and radio wavelengths, which are more easily able to pass through gas and dust. I'll talk about that later.

The pictures from Hubble have been stunning. The spectroscopy that Hubble has done has also been stunning, but you can't so easily visually portray it, so I don't show it. After pictures like this were published, there were new headlines. One of them, "Heaven Can Wait." Another said something like, "Heaven Photographed by Hubble Telescope." I'm not going to go into religion here. You can believe it or you cannot believe it, but I don't think that any of the NASA astronomers who have data claim that they have actually seen where heaven is. So don't believe everything you read in various reputable or not so reputable journals. "We Found Where God Lives, Says Scientist," read one. The scientist who reputedly said that was probably fired.

It's a smashing success and much of the work that I'll be discussing in these forty lectures will have stemmed from the Hubble Space Telescope in that I'm going to be emphasizing contemporary modern astronomy in these lectures. Certainly, the space telescope has provided data that have really revolutionized some of our views of the cosmos.

NASA is now working on plans for an eight-meter diameter space telescope. The Hubble Space Telescope is only 2.4 meters in diameter. NASA wants to build an eight-meter diameter space telescope with which it can search for planets and look at the birth of galaxies and things like that. That'll probably be built in about a decade.

The Shuttle crew who did this fix were heroes. Those seven men and women did a tremendous job and we, as astronomers, owe a tremendous debt of gratitude to them.

I'd like to now move on to the celestial sphere, the view of the night sky, the stars, and their motions. What do we perceive here from the surface of the Earth? When we look at the night sky the things that we mostly obviously see are stars, these bright points of light that have for such a long time mystified people. Of course, we now know that they are distant suns, like our own. For a long time, they were just mysterious little points of light.

The ancients grouped these into patterns. Here we see Leo the lion. Here's Leo's tail, the body, and then the sickle of Leo is the head. They actually look like a lion. Scorpios looks like a scorpion. Orion the hunter looks like a person, like a hunter. Most of the constellations don't look like what they are named after. They were largely named in honor of the beasts, people or gods that are their names. They don't really look like these objects.

People wanted to form patterns in the sky and they wanted to see how these patterns rose and fell with the seasons so, they could know when to plant their crops, when the Nile was going to flood and things like that. It was useful for people to make these patterns.

There are 88 of these so-called constellations recognized in modern times. Every star belongs to one and only one constellation. Most of them are now named in honor of Greek heroes, although Egyptian, Mexican, and South American cultures all had their own stories to go along with these things. Most of the surviving ones, at least in the Western world, are named after Greek heroes.

Some of the ones in the Southern Hemisphere have names like Microscopium and Telescopium because the ancient Greeks did not know about the far southern skies, did not see those constellations, and hadn't named them yet.

There are also things called asterisms. The Big Dipper, here's the bowl of the dipper and there's the handle, is part of a much bigger grouping of stars called Ursa Major, the Great Bear. How you get a bear out of this is a little bit beyond me. The Big Dipper, part of the constellation, is called an asterism. It's a familiar grouping of stars, which is not in and of itself an entire constellation, so there are asterisms and there are constellations.

You might think that the stars in a given constellation, being relatively close to each other, are somehow associated with one another. They're at the same distance, or formed or bound together. That, in general, turns out not to be the case. The apparent patterns of the constellations are simply accidental patterns that occur because stars at different distances happen to line up with one another. Most of the stars in most constellations have no physical relationship to each other. It is as though you are looking through a crowd of people and you see nearby people lined up with distant people. Though they appear close in angular distance from each other, they have no physical relationship with each other.

The Big Dipper is actually a little bit of a counter example to that. You can see here that five of the seven stars are about at the same distance. Not quite at the same distance, between sixty and ninety light years away. They're clearly not physically bound, being separated by tens of light years, but they are at least reasonably close together; and they did form from the same nebula, or cloud of gas and dust. To our first approximation, they're moving into the same direction of the heavens with each other. But the other two stars are clearly quite a bit more distant and in fact are moving in an opposite direction. Even the Big Dipper consists of stars at different distances and physically unrelated to each other, although five of the seven stars in the Big Dipper are, in fact, physically related to each other, so that's a bit of a counter example.

Here in this slide, you can actually see the motion of the seven stars and the Big Dipper. Five of them are moving roughly to the left, as seen in this diagram, and the end star of the handle, as well as the tip of the bowl, are moving very slowly through the sky in roughly the opposite direction. In fact, if you were to have looked at the Big Dipper 50,000 years ago, this is what it would have appeared like. It's handle wouldn't have been quite as bent at the end, and the bowl wouldn't have been quite as well formed, because the tip star of the bowl would have been squashed toward the other three a little bit more.

Fifty thousand years from today, the Big Dipper's shape will have changed again. It changes continuously, of course, but the handle will be more bent and the bowl will be lengthened a little bit because these two stars at the ends are moving in different directions than the other stars. So the constellations change in shape slowly over tens of thousands of years.

Now let's consider the entire celestial sphere, not just constellations within them. Let's define two quantities. The zenith is just the point in the sky directly over you. Look straight up; that's the zenith. The horizon is 90°, one quarter of a circle, down from the zenith in whatever direction you choose to look. There might be mountains in the way or trees or buildings. Those produce a false horizon. That is not your true horizon. You know that when the sun sets behind a house, it doesn't suddenly become dark. It has to set below the true horizon.

The true horizon is what you get when you look along the surface of the Earth. If you were to look further down, you would be looking through the surface of the Earth, which you can't do. That's your horizon.

If we look at the celestial sphere, it's as though the stars were plastered on a sphere very far away from us. To our first approximation, we can't tell how far away the stars are, at least not with our naked eye. It kind of looks as though they are just plastered on a sphere very far away and that sphere rotates around us. That's what we call the celestial sphere.

The zenith is just the point directly over you on the celestial sphere. Your horizon is the plane or in this case the great circle in the sky, which is the intersection of the plane tangent to where you're standing, and the celestial sphere. That's your horizon.

A projection of Earth's equator onto the celestial sphere produces the celestial equator. It's just a great circle, which is a circle produced by a plane passing through the center of the sphere. Airplanes travel largely on great circles to minimize the distances, for example. That's the celestial equator.

The celestial poles are simply the extensions of the North and South Poles. Here's the south celestial pole and here's the north celestial pole. The whole thing kind of rotates around these poles because the Earth is spinning around its axis.

There's one other curve that I'd like to define, which isn't shown here; that's the meridian. The meridian is the curve, or great circle, passing through your zenith due south and due north. It's, in a sense, the highest point in the sky to which any star appears to rise. When the star is due south, it is crossing the meridian. It's the great circle going from north to south through the zenith.

Let's consider what we would see if we looked at the stars. We can assign each star a coordinate, much like we assign a coordinate to every point on the surface of the Earth. The latitude of a city is just the number of degrees, or the fraction of the circle, above (for north) or below (for south) the Earth's equator. The longitude is the number of degrees away from some arbitrary point. In this case, on Earth it's the prime meridian, the great circle passing through Greenwich, England. That's the arbitrary point from which we measure longitude.

On the sky, we have the declination, which is the corresponding coordinate of latitude and the right ascension, which is the corresponding coordinate of longitude. The zero point for right ascension happens to be the vernal equinox, the place in the sky where the Sun is the first day of spring. We can define coordinates in the sky for every star that we observe.

Why is it that we see only half of the celestial sphere at any given moment, from any given position? If you were placed here on Earth, you would define your horizon, effectively, by the tangent to the Earth. You can't look through the Earth; you can only see things that are above the Earth, so that defines your horizon. If the celestial sphere were close to the Earth, then the only parts of the celestial sphere that we could see would be this part above the horizon. That would clearly be less than half of the full celestial sphere.

If the celestial sphere were farther away, then the arc that we can see is clearly a bigger fraction of the total than was the case when the celestial sphere was small. If the celestial sphere is very far away, you can see that the arc is nearly one half of the full circle. If the celestial sphere is, effectively, infinitely far away—and compared to the size of the Earth, the stars are infinitely far away—you can see that what we can examine at any given time, from any given point with a clear horizon, is half of the celestial sphere.

Let's place ourselves on the North Pole of the Earth. What would we see? I claim that we would see the stars circling around the north celestial pole never changing their altitude above the horizon. Different stars would have different altitudes above the horizon and stars right on the celestial equator would be right on your horizon because that would define the limit of the celestial sphere that you see.

It's as though you're a little girl standing on the pole of the world and the world is turning underneath you. Your feet are planted on Earth so they go around with it. You see first this direction, then that direction, and then that direction and so on. But you never see the stars in the Southern Hemisphere, the stars that are below the celestial equator, because you're orientation relative to the celestial equator never changes.

If, on the other hand, we're standing on the equator, which is shown here, then the axis of the Earth is perpendicular to our location or our direction from the center of the Earth and it's as though the Earth rotates out from underneath us, but the opposite way. The celestial poles are on the horizon. Stars appear to rise straight up, go through graceful arcs and set down in the west. They rise in the east and set in the west and all stars will do that. They will just rise straight up, go over and set straight down like this.

You can see that throughout the course of a 24-hour day, your line of sight would intersect the entire celestial sphere. Let's go back to my girl here who, suppose now, is on the equator. Let's make this the poles now; I don't want to change her location. The Earth is spinning and you can see that her perspective changes. She's seeing me now. Now she's seeing you over there. Now she's seeing you, and finally you and so on, and back to me.

So, she can see the entire celestial sphere over the course of 24 hours; only 12 of those hours will be dark; but, in principle, the entire celestial sphere is visible. Whereas, from the poles, even in principal, only half of the celestial sphere is visible, because you never rotate out from under the Earth like this.

At intermediate locations, you can see that you have a combination of those two motions. Some of the stars will be above the horizon, some stars will be below the horizon and most stars will rise sort of at an angle, cross the sky and set at an angle. This is illustrated with a photograph, here, showing the stars rise at an angle from the horizon, go up and then complete a loop around, and set at an angle relative to the horizon. They go neither in perfect circles at a constant altitude above the Earth's surface, nor do they rise straight up and set straight down. They do something intermediately.

You'll notice that some of the stars are above the horizon at all times. Those are called circumpolar stars. Again, it might not be dark at all times, but they will be above the horizon at all times, whereas other stars go below the horizon and are not even in principle seen at all times. The pole star is above the horizon all the time and the stars near the pole are above the horizon.

Here, in fact, you can see a picture of the Earth's north celestial pole. The star Polaris is near it. All these stars near Polaris are above Earth's horizon as viewed from the latitude of all cities in the United States all the time. The closer you are to the pole, the greater the fraction of the celestial sphere that is always above the horizon. The down side is the fraction of the total celestial sphere you can see is smaller, even in principal. So, on the equator there are no circumpolar stars. The poles are right on the horizon but you can see the whole celestial sphere. At the poles, all stars are circumpolar but you can only see half of the celestial sphere.

By the way, our pole star, Polaris, happens to be a fairly bright star. It won't always be there because our axis of rotation is actually very slowly changing orientation every 26,000 years. That's because the gravitational tugs of the Sun and the Moon cause it to wobble a little bit. But for all intents and purposes, over our lifetime Polaris will be the pole star.

In the Southern Hemisphere shown here, there is no bright star near the pole. They're just unlucky right now. We will be unlucky later on when our Polaris star moves away.

Now let's look at how the night sky changes over the course of a year. How does our year of a night sky change with the seasons? Here's the Sun in the middle and here's the Earth. In December, at midnight, the constellation Orion is visible nearly overhead. If you're on the equator, it's actually right overhead. You can tell this is midnight here on Earth because we're halfway between sunset and sunrise. You're on the point on Earth, which is most shaded from the Sun. That's midnight looking this way.

In March, three months later, the Earth's orientation is like this, compared with the Sun. It is rotated over by 90°. At midnight you view a different set of stars. They happen to be the stars of Virgo. The direction of Orion—remember Orion is very far away and all the light rays are coming in parallel—is seen at sunset. This is the sunset point on Earth. It's the point going from the sunlit part to the dark part. At sunset, looking right at the horizon, you would see Orion.

If you're seeing Orion at sunset in March and at midnight in December, that means that over the course of three months (90 days), the stars will appear to have shifted effectively by six hours. The difference in time between sunset and midnight is six hours. Sunset is around 6:00 p.m.; midnight is around 12:00. In the course of 90 days, our view of the sky has shifted by six hours. We're seeing Orion six hours earlier than we did in December. In March we see it six hours earlier.

Ninety days times four minutes per day equal 360 minutes. That's six hours. Clearly this is a continuous process. With each day, the stars reach the overhead point or rise or set four minutes earlier; it doesn't matter which you take. Each day that you look at the sky a given star will rise four minutes earlier so that over the course of ninety days, those four minutes per day times ninety days will be 360 minutes, or six hours. That means Orion will be visible on the horizon at sunset in March versus overhead at midnight in December.

Microscopically, here's what's happening. Suppose I am the Earth and the podium is the Sun and you are a star over there. I'm lining up the Sun and you right now. I can't see you during the day, but let's forget about the fact that it's bright for a moment. I see you at noon directly overhead. In one day, what will happen? I will rotate once like this and I will see you in the camera when I'm pointing back at you but the Sun will not yet be overhead. I have to rotate a little bit more over like this, an extra bit, to see the Sun because I will have moved roughly one degree along my orbit in that one day. The Earth moves 360°, a full circuit, around the Sun in 365 days, so it moves about one degree per day. In that one day, I will have moved over. So when a given star is overhead once again after one day, the Sun will not yet be overhead. I actually have to rotate for another four minutes, 3:56 to be precise, but four minutes among friends. That is what leads to the rising of the stars four minutes earlier each day. Our clocks are set by solar time, not sidereal time, the time of the stars.

Now let us consider the seasons. The seasons are caused not by differing distances of the Earth from the Sun, which is one of the common misconceptions; nor by some sort of a crazy flip that the Earth does on its axis in sort of flopping back and forth, which is another popular misconception. Rather it's due to the fact that Earth's orientation on its axis is tilted by 23.5°, relative to the perpendicular to the orbital plane. That axis tilt means that at some times of the year, the Northern Hemisphere is sort of pointed toward the Sun. Yes, it's a little bit closer to the Sun than the Southern Hemisphere, but that's not the point here. The distance is not the point. It's angled toward the Sun and the Southern Hemisphere is angled away from the Sun. In fact, the South Pole gets hidden from the Sun entirely and the North Pole is always in the Sun's light.

Six months later, when the Earth has gone to this position relative to the Sun, its axis of rotation will have remained fixed. It doesn't flip-flop physically in space, but rather as it orbits the Sun, the axis remains pointed in the same direction. It's like a spinning top left alone in space; the spinning top does not want to change its orientation. It has what's called angular momentum. Unless you do something to that top, such as try to flip it over, it will remain pointing in the same direction.

About six months later, then, if the Earth is pointing in the same direction, what will happen? The Southern Hemisphere of the Earth will be tilted preferentially to the Sun and the Northern Hemisphere of the Earth will be tilted preferentially away from the Sun.

Let me illustrate that with this demonstration. I have the Sun, which is this globe, and the Earth, whose axis is tilted by 23.5° away from the perpendicular, the normal to the orbital plane. Let's forget about Venus and the Moon, for the purposes of this demonstration. Right now, I've oriented things so that it is summer in the Northern Hemisphere. The North Pole in fact is pointing completely at the Sun. It's in the Sun's light all times of the day so you have the phenomenon of the midnight sun. The Southern Hemisphere cannot see the Sun at all. People there would have to look through the Earth or a tube or hole in the Earth in order to see the Sun. The Sun is below the horizon. In fact, at the South Pole, the Sun is below the horizon for about six months of the year and above the horizon for about six months of the year continuously.

If I now rotate the Earth around the Sun as it orbits the Sun, you can see that the orientation of the Earth's axis has not changed. It is still pointing that way up there, as it was when it was on this side of the Sun. Now, the Northern Hemisphere is tilted away and the Southern Hemisphere is tilted towards the Sun. It would be summer in the Southern Hemisphere and winter in the Northern Hemisphere.

At points in between, you can see that neither the North Pole nor the South Pole is preferentially tilted towards the Sun. Those are the equinoxes when in fact in spring and fall the nights are roughly equally long everywhere on Earth.

What then produces the heating effect? Notice in this diagram that in the Northern Hemisphere summer, say, June 22, the arc of the Sun above the horizon is this big loop. It spends relatively little of its time below the horizon. This is drawn as an intermediate latitude, as is most of the United States. At the poles, the Sun would look like it's above the horizon all the time, but in the Northern Hemisphere, it's above the celestial equator, because we're pointed towards it, so the arc that it goes through day-to-day is quite long. It spends most of its time there. That means that the Earth's surface gets heated and is illuminated for much of the day. You get sunlight for much of the day.

The most obvious manifestation of the seasons is not whether it's cold or warm outside, because you can have warm days in the winter and awfully cold days in the summer. Mark Twain once said, "The coldest day I ever spent was a summer day in San Francisco," or something to that effect. The most obvious manifestation of the seasons is the changing of the day and night. It is always true that the day is long in the summer in the Northern Hemisphere, that is it is above the horizon. Whether you can see it or not is immaterial, but it is above the horizon always in the summer for a long time. Likewise, it is always below the horizon for a long time in the winter. So the length of the day is clearly related to how the Sun is above the horizon, and you can see that it is above the horizon for a long time in this diagram.

Now let's look at the diagram from the perspective of someone watching the sky on the days of the equinoxes, March 21 or 22 and September 23. Then the Earth is oriented in such a way that the Sun illuminates the equator from directly overhead. It doesn't illuminate either of the poles most directly. In addition, the Sun is right on the celestial equator, so it's up half the time and down below the horizon about half the time. Then, in the dead of winter, as seen from the Northern Hemisphere, the Sun is below the celestial equator. So its arc above the horizon is small and the arc below the horizon is large. This leads to a short day and a long night in the winter.

Now let's look at the heating effect. When the sunlight directly illuminates the Earth's surface; that is, when the Sun is high (direct), then a given bundle of light, say, one meter squared in area or one meter in length, like this, it illuminates 1.04 square meters of the ground. So, you've got pretty direct illumination. The light is coming pretty much straight down, and the bundle of light is not being spread out over a very large area.

But if the sun is close to the horizon, then that bundle of light is spread out over a larger area. Here's that same bundle of light coming down, one square meter's worth. The meter that goes in and out of the plane of the television is unaffected, but the meter that is in the plane of the television intersects at an angle relative to the

Earth's surface and that in projection becomes 2.24 meters. So the total, in fact, at this angle of illumination, 27° or 26, is 2.34 square meters. The same bundle of light was spread out over a larger area on Earth's surface. Therefore, per unit area, the surface of the Earth got less sunlight and less heating. That then leads to the colder temperatures. It is heated less per unit area and the day is shorter during the winter months.

At the poles, as I mentioned, you can see the midnight sun. Here is a view taken by one of the students at the University of California at Berkeley of the midnight sun from the South Pole. He was doing research there. Here's sunset at the South Pole. "Goodbye, Sun, we're not going to see you for about six months." Actually, it turns out to be about five months because the Earth's atmosphere bends the sunlight up a little bit; there's a refraction effect. So, when you see the Sun setting on the horizon, it has actually set in the real world already but it stays up a little bit longer. Also, the top part of the Sun is above the horizon before the bottom part and that makes the seasons not quite the same length as well. It's down for about six months and up for about six months. The seasons are simply defined that the beginning of summer in the Northern Hemisphere is June 22 when the Sun is at its highest point, the equinoxes are in March and September, and winter is in December.

Perhaps paradoxically, summer is defined to be that moment of the year when the Sun achieves its highest point in the sky. From then on, it's all downhill. You might think that summer should be better defined to be symmetrically located about that point But that's just not the way it is, partly, I think, because there's a seasonal lag as to when the atmosphere and the water actually get their hottest temperatures.

Lecture Seven
Our Sun—The Nearest Star

Scope:

Stars are large, luminous spheres of gas held together by gravity. The surface temperature of a star determines its apparent color: hot stars are bluer than cool ones. Moreover, per unit of surface area, hot stars are far more powerful than cool stars. These are general characteristics of objects that emit light due to random ("thermal") motions of their constituent particles. In the case of a perfect thermal emitter, the shape of the electromagnetic spectrum depends only on the temperature, and the object is known as a "black body." This approximation is very useful for some aspects of stellar studies. The Sun, a typical but exceptionally nearby star, can be investigated in great detail. Sunspots are relatively cool, dark regions of the solar surface that are associated with strong magnetic fields. The number of sunspots and gaseous eruptions visible on the Sun varies over an 11-year period known as the solar activity cycle.

Objectives

Upon completion of this lecture, you should be able to:

1. Describe briefly what the Sun is, and how it is related to stars.
2. Define what is meant by the surface (photosphere) of a star.
3. Explain what physicists mean by the term "black body."
4. Discuss qualitatively the spectra of black bodies with different temperatures but the same surface area.
5. Calculate the wavelength at which the spectrum of a black body peaks, given its temperature.
6. Explain why a sunspot looks dark.
7. Summarize the different parts of the Sun above the photosphere, including ephemeral phenomena.

Outline

I. Stars are huge, opaque, luminous balls of gas held together by the mutual gravitational attraction of their constituent particles.

   A. There are about 400 billion stars in our Milky Way Galaxy. The Sun is typical in size, but much closer to us than any other star.

B. The very hot, dense, ionized inner parts of a star emit continuous radiation (a "continuum"); many physical processes smear out the discrete emission lines that are characteristic of low-density gases.

C. Cooler, less dense outer layers of gas absorb certain wavelengths in the manner discussed previously.

    1. The chemical composition can be determined by analysis of the absorption lines.

    2. This is how we know that stars consist of normal elements found on Earth!

D. The outer atmosphere of a star is transparent, and the "surface" (photosphere) is simply the region beyond which the gases are opaque. This surface radiates light into space.

E. The wavelength of the peak (brightest part) of the star's spectrum, which determines the color of the star, is a measure of its surface temperature, as explained below.

II. Ignoring absorption lines, which are generally weak, the spectrum of a star resembles that of a "black body."

A. A black body absorbs all incident radiation; none is transmitted or reflected. It is a "perfect absorber."

B. A black body has a certain *temperature*, which is a measure of the average speed with which constituent particles (atoms, molecules) jiggle around: the higher the temperature, the greater the average speed.

C. The randomly moving particles, some of which are charged, emit electromagnetic radiation. This is called thermal radiation.

D. The shape of the spectrum emitted by a black body depends only on the object's temperature, not on its chemical composition or other properties. It is a "perfect emitter."

E. This spectral shape is called the Planck curve, in honor of the physicist Max Planck; its derivation was a fundamental problem in quantum mechanics.

F. At all wavelengths, the spectrum (Planck curve) of a hot black body is higher (i.e., brighter) than that of a colder black body having the same surface area.

G. An important property is that the spectrum of a hot black body peaks at a shorter wavelength than the spectrum of a colder black body.

   1. Thus, if one heats an iron ball with a powerful torch, it first glows dull red, then orange, followed by white (a combination of colors, like sunlight), and eventually blue.

   2. Some quantitative examples: at temperatures of 4000 K, 5000 K, 6000 K, and 7000 K, the peak of the black body spectrum is at wavelengths of 7200 Å, 5800 Å, 4800 Å, and 4100 Å, respectively.

   3. The product of the temperature (T) and the peak wavelength (λ_{max}) is a constant: $\lambda_{max}T = 2.9 \times 10^7$ Å K. This is known as Wien's law.

   4. Note that a human (which can be approximated as a black body with T ≈ 300 K) emits *thermally* at infrared wavelengths (~10^5 Å, or 10 μm, according to Wien's law).

     a. Thus, we can be seen with infrared detectors even at night.

     b. We are visible at *optical* wavelengths, however, only because of *reflected* light (e.g., sunlight, or light from indoor bulbs). This has nothing to do with our thermal emission.

H. Per unit of surface area, a hot black body emits much more energy per second than a cold black body.

   1. This is known at the Stefan-Boltzmann law.

   2. It can be expressed mathematically as $E = \sigma T^4$, where E is the energy emitted per unit area (e.g., cm^2) per second, T is the temperature, and σ is a constant (known as the Stefan-Boltzmann constant).

   3. For example, if two stars have the same surface area, but one is twice as hot as the other, the hotter star emits $2^4 = 16$ times as much energy (per second) as the colder star.

   4. However, in the above example, if the hotter star's radius R is ¼ that of the colder star, then its surface area is $(1/4)^2 = 1/16$ as large as that of the colder star, because the surface area of a sphere is given by $4\pi R^2$. This exactly balances the greater emission per unit area, making the two stars equally luminous (i.e., equal power, or total energy emitted per second).

5. In general, the luminosity (L) of a black body is given by its surface area (S) multiplied by the energy emitted per unit area per second (E): L = SE.

   a. For a sphere of radius R and temperature T, we have $L = 4\pi R^2 \sigma T^4$.

   b. Thus, if we know the luminosity and surface temperature of a star, we can derive its radius R.

III. The Sun, being only 1 AU (150 million km) away, can be studied in considerable detail.

A. Its visible surface (photosphere) subtends about half a degree in the sky.

   1. At the Sun's distance, this corresponds to a diameter of 1.4×10^6 km.

   2. Given that the Earth's diameter is about 1.3×10^4 km, about 110 Earths could fit across the diameter of the Sun.

   3. The Sun's volume is therefore over a million (110^3) times that of the Earth.

   4. However, as we will derive later, the Sun's mass is only about 330,000 Earth masses, so its average density is lower than that of the Earth.

B. The Sun's spectrum peaks at about 5000 Å.

   1. According to Wien's law, the Sun's surface temperature is therefore about 5800 K.

   2. 5000 Å corresponds to green light. However, the overall black-body spectrum of the Sun is perceived by the human eye as *white* light, not yellow as is usually taught.

      a. This can be very clearly seen during a total solar eclipse: seconds before totality, only a tiny part of the Sun's photosphere is uncovered, and it can be viewed safely with the unaided eye. It has a dazzling white color, if the Sun is high in the sky.

      b. The Sun appears yellow, or even orange or red, when it is approaching the horizon and generally safer to examine; gas and dust in the thicker atmosphere preferentially scatter and absorb the blue-green wavelengths.

3. It is probably no accident that human eyes are most sensitive to electromagnetic radiation near the peak of the Sun's spectrum, and to which Earth's atmosphere is transparent.

IV. Sunspots are dark blotches on the photosphere.

   A. Some of them are visible to the unaided eye (through a filter), and hence are much larger than the Earth. The approximate rotation period of the Sun (~1 month) can be measured by monitoring large, long-lived sunspots.

   B. Spectra show that sunspots are about 2000 K cooler than the surrounding photosphere.
      1. According to the Stefan-Boltzmann law they are less luminous per unit area, and hence appear darker.
      2. However, if the gas in a sunspot were plucked from the Sun and viewed alone, it would glow brightly; many stars have surface temperatures of 3800 K.

   C. Sunspots are regions of strong, tangled magnetic fields.
      1. These fields inhibit the rise of hot, ionized gas from below the photosphere, so the regions cool down.
      2. Away from sunspots, the Sun's magnetic field is reasonably simple. Globally, it resembles that of a bar magnet.

   D. When observed in excellent viewing conditions, the Sun's photosphere appears somewhat grainy.
      1. The bright granules are hot, rising, convective cells (pockets of gas) that bring energy from the interior to the surface.
      2. This is analogous to blobs of water carrying energy from the bottom of a heated pot to the eggs floating on top.
      3. After releasing its heat, the gas is denser, and it sinks back down. This cooler gas appears darker than its surroundings because of the Stefan-Boltzmann law: less light is emitted per unit area.

V. Besides the photosphere, the main external components of the Sun are as follows.

   A. The chromosphere is a thin layer (about 10^4 km thick) immediately above the photosphere.
      1. Its temperature is about 10^4 K, hotter than the photosphere.

2. The heating is probably mechanical: rising pockets of gas deposit their energy of motion (kinetic energy) in the chromosphere.
3. It glows with a red color because the electrons in many hydrogen atoms are jumping from the third to the second energy level, producing the Balmer-α (Hα) emission line.
4. The chromosphere is most easily seen during a total solar eclipse, as discussed later.

B. The corona is a large, low-density envelope of very hot gas.
  1. Its temperature can reach 2 million degrees.
     a. It emits x-rays.
     b. Spectra show that many of the atoms are highly ionized, as would be the case if they were experiencing high-speed collisions.
     c. The heating mechanism is probably a combination of mechanical heating (as with the chromosphere) and release of energy stored in magnetic fields.
     d. Although the temperature is high, the total heat content is low because the gas is so tenuous.
  2. It has complex structure due to charged particles traveling along magnetic fields.
  3. Essentially the only time one can see it is during a total solar eclipse.

C. The solar wind is a stream of charged particles (mostly electrons and protons) streaming from the Sun at speeds of up to 500 km/s. It interacts with planetary magnetic fields and with comets.

D. A solar flare is a violent release of energy from a localized region of the Sun's surface.
  1. Temperatures can reach 5 million degrees.
  2. Large numbers of emitted charged particles interact with Earth's atmosphere and produce disturbances in radio communications.

E. A prominence is a more gentle eruption from the Sun's surface.
  1. Gas tends to follow magnetic field lines, producing beautiful loops.
  2. The gas temperature is about 10^4 K.
  3. As in the chromosphere, the loops glow with a red color.

VI. The Sun goes through an activity cycle.

    A. The number of visible sunspots varies over a period of about 11 years.

        1. There should be a maximum around the year 2001.

        2. During solar maximum there can be over 100 spots at any given time, while at solar minimum the number drops to only a few.

        3. Solar maximum is also characterized by a large number of ephemeral phenomena such as prominences and flares.

        4. Since the magnetic polarity of sunspots changes every 11 years (i.e., north-south pairs, followed by south-north), the period of the solar activity cycle can be thought of as 22 years instead of 11 years.

    B. The solar activity cycle is the manifestation of a complex dynamo; details are not yet understood.

        1. The Sun's rotation period is shorter at the equator (~ 25 days) than near the poles (~ 33 days), so it doesn't behave like a solid body.

        2. This "differential rotation" stretches and tangles magnetic field lines, giving rise to sunspots.

Essential Reading:

Kippenhahn, R. *Discovering the Secrets of the Sun*. Wiley, 1994.

Kirkpatrick, L., and Wheeler, G. *Physics: A World View*, 2nd edition. Saunders, 1995.

Wentzel, D. *The Restless Sun*. Smithsonian Inst. Press, 1989.

Questions to Consider:

1. In what ways are humans not a good approximation to black bodies? Why do astronomers and physicists use the concept of a black body, when theoretically such objects are almost nonexistent?

2. Try to put yourself in the position of the ancients. What would you think if someone suggested that the stars are simply very distant suns?

3. Consider a sunspot viewed through a dark filter or reasonably thick fog. If the sunspot is barely visible to the unaided eye (which has a resolution of about 1 or 2 arc minutes), and the Sun's diameter is 30 arc minutes, physically how large is the sunspot relative to the Earth?

Lecture Seven—Transcript
Our Sun—The Nearest Star

When you look out into the dark night sky, you see a tremendous number of stars. Here in this picture, you can see the Milky Way Galaxy. In fact, in the direction of the center of our galaxy, this is what we see—a vast number of stars, giant clouds of stars. We estimate that there are roughly 400 billion stars in our MWG. Our galaxy is reasonably large, but not atypically so. Here is another galaxy that also has a few hundred billion stars.

What are the stars? What are these points of light? It turns out that the stars are like the Sun. They are distant suns, just so far away that we cannot see the disks of which they consist. Our Sun is so nearby, that the angle that it subtends in the sky, its size in the sky, is about half a degree. Knowing the distance of the Sun, we can then calculate that it is about 1.4 million kilometers across. I think I used 1.5 million in Lecture II, but that was just an approximation.

It's a gigantic ball, or sphere, of hot glowing gas gravitationally bound to itself. All the little particles are pulling on all the other little particles, keeping it together. Other stars are like our Sun but are just too distant to see.

If we look at what produces the light of our Sun, it's the hot gases in the interior. Later, we will see that that energy is generated by nuclear reactions in the core. The light that is generated by those nuclear reactions makes its way out through the Sun bouncing around for a very long time, until finally it is emitted by the surface of the Sun. What we mean by the surface of the Sun, or of any star, is simply the layer from which the light can escape. Below that layer, the gases are opaque; you cannot see through them. The photons are all bouncing and jiggling around many times. Finally they reach a region where the density, the amount of gas per unit volume, is so small that they are able to fly freely through space and escape from the star. That is what we call the surface of the Sun or the surface of a star. There is no solid physical surface. There is just the apparent surface from which the photons appear to radiate.

The gas within the star is very hot and all the atoms jiggle around a tremendous amount. That's what heat or temperature is, a measure of how quickly atoms, particles and electrons are jostling around. They hit one another. In fact, they hit one another so hard that much of the

Sun's interior is completely ionized. The very central regions, in fact, are very highly ionized. All of the electrons have been stripped away from atoms by these violent collisions. Even in the outer parts of the Sun, a few of the electrons from some of the elements have been lost by collisions.

There's a lot of jostling around and a lot of atoms and electrons hitting each other. Electrons get stripped away. All this jostling produces smeared emission and absorption lines. You don't have a very narrow wavelength range at which a particular electronic transition can occur, as was the case when I described my simple atom that was sitting alone in space not troubled by any others. There the energy levels were quite well defined. But, if the atoms are jostling against each other, then the energy levels are smeared and there are free electrons moving around as well. All these complicated physical processes give rise to smeared lines, which in total form are what we call a continuous spectrum. If you plot the brightness of the Sun, or a star, versus the color or wavelength of its light to a first approximation, what you get is a smeared continuum, a smooth continuum that is produced by the totality of all electrons and atoms interacting with radiation or photons inside the star, and producing a very smeared spectrum.

In the outer most parts of the star, the atoms are reasonably cool and don't move that fast, and are either neutral or ionized only once or twice; one or two of the electrons might be missing. Those cool atoms, which retain some of their electrons, can absorb the hot continuum produced from within. They can absorb that continuum at specific quite narrowly defined wavelength ranges. So, it is those outermost relatively cool parts of the Sun and the stars that produce the absorption lines that we see in their spectra.

If you look at the solar spectrum—here it is—you can see that there are in fact quite a few absorption lines. The Earth's atmosphere causes a few of these, such as this one here and that one there. That is actually caused by molecular oxygen in our atmosphere. Essentially all of the other dark streaks that you see here are produced by different elements and different ions of these elements absorbing specific wavelengths according to their undisturbed energy levels. They're reasonably undisturbed because the cool outer parts of the star do not jostle the atoms and electrons around it too much.

The lines are fairly narrow; they appear at the wavelengths that they normally have and one can measure those wavelengths and deduce what kinds of elements are present. We see sodium, magnesium, hydrogen, and all sorts of elements, calcium down here, carbon. All sorts of elements are seen in the spectrum of the Sun. As I emphasized a few lectures ago, this is how we know that the Sun consists of the same sorts of elements that we have here on Earth, maybe not in the same proportions. The Sun has far more hydrogen than what we have on Earth, but the same kinds of elements exist. The stars that are light years or thousands of light years away, in a similar manner, consist of the same sorts of elements. The universe out there does not have a different periodic table than our local environment. It's all made out of the same stuff, and this is how astronomers know. They know from the spectra of the stars.

Something that you notice when you look at the stars at night is that they actually have slightly different colors, very subtly different colors. By and large, they look mostly white, but a few of them look orange or perhaps even red. Some of them look bluer than others. This is most easily seen if you allow your camera shutter to remain open for a while and let the stars streak across the sky reflecting the rotation of the Earth. That's how all of these pictures were produced that I have shown, by stars going around in arcs across the sky. The shutter of the camera was simply left open for a length of time.

When you do that, the colors are more easily visible than if you track the motion of the stars because the stars smear out a little bit, and you can actually see their colors more easily. Those colors, it turns out, are a reflection of the temperature of the surface of the star, the temperature of the gases from which the radiation is able to escape. The star is hotter on the inside and cooler on the outside, and it's that surface from which they escape whose temperature you're measuring when you look at the color of a star.

The cooler stars look redder and the hotter stars look whiter, and eventually even bluer for the hottest stars. Let's see how that occurs. When we look at the spectrum, we see that there's light at many different wavelengths throughout the spectrum, with some absorption lines as well. But the peak is at a particular wavelength and, to a first approximation, that peak wavelength tells you the color of the star. If the peak is in the red part of the spectrum, the star will look red. If the peak is in the blue part of the spectrum, the star will look blue.

It turns out that, physiologically, our eyes perceive as white the distribution of wavelengths that peaks in the green part of the spectrum but has some non-zero amount of light at other parts of the spectrum. We call that white light and, indeed, sunlight is white light. It is not green light. It peaks in the green, but it looks white, physiologically.

Let's take a look at the shape of the curve emitted by a star. If we ignore the absorption lines in the spectrum of a star, the curve looks smooth and has a shape that looks something like this. It rises from very small values at ultraviolet wavelengths up to some peak at visible or infrared wavelengths, and then it decreases down again as you go farther toward ultraviolet wavelengths. Different stars, having different surface temperatures, have curves that appear roughly the same shape mathematically but have different heights. A hotter star has a higher intensity curve than a cooler star.

It turns out that that particular shape for the curve is very characteristic of objects whose spectrum depends only on their temperature, not on any other property: not on their chemical composition, not on their mass—not on anything—except their temperature. Admittedly, a real star's spectrum has some absorption lines and those depend on its chemical composition and other things. But those are weak little deviations from this smooth, featureless spectrum. If you ignore the absorption lines, stars have what's called, basically, a black body spectrum.

A black body is sort of a funny term that physicists have dreamed up for an object that emits a spectrum that is only dependent on its temperature. After all, you might think that a black body shouldn't emit any light at all. So, what are we talking about a black body emitting light? By black body, we mean an object that is a perfect absorber and a perfect emitter. By that, I mean that it absorbs all the light incident upon it. Nothing is reflected; all of it is absorbed. Indeed, black paper looks at least at visible wavelengths like a black body because none of the light is reflected. All of it is absorbed.

For an ideal black body, none is reflected at any wavelength. No matter what wavelength light you shine on the body, all of that light, all of that electromagnetic radiation is absorbed. None is reflected.

What happens to the energy deposited in a black body by all this incident radiation? It heats up the substance of which that black body is made. It makes the atoms and molecules and whatever jostle around more. As they heat up, they jostle around more because temperature is just a measure of how much motion there is among the subatomic particles of which the substance consists.

A black body absorbs radiation, it heats up and jostles around, but these little particles are charged. Electrons and nuclei of atoms are charged. Charged particles that are moving every which way—first this way, then that way, and so on—emit electromagnetic radiation. They are accelerated charged particles and accelerated particles emit radiation. If the body is dense enough, hot enough or opaque enough, and all these things are jostling around, light cannot get through that object. All of the light gets absorbed. We've defined this to be a black body. All of the incident radiation goes into heating up the particles.

Because they then re-radiate energy due to the accelerations caused by bumping into one another, that re-radiation has this characteristic shape known as black body, or thermal radiation. The black body does not heat up to an infinitely high temperature. It starts radiating energy until the rate at which it radiates energy balances the rate at which energy is absorbed from the outside. At that point, the black body reaches an equilibrium temperature. It is absorbing radiation just as fast as it is re-emitting radiation. None of the radiation is being reflected in a classical sense. All of it is being absorbed. Bits and pieces jostle around and, then they re-radiate that radiation. That kind of radiation produces this characteristic black body, or thermal spectrum.

The mathematical derivation of the shape of the spectrum was one of the great triumphs of early 20th century quantum physics. Indeed, it is this shape of a black body emitter that was so hard to understand from the perspective of purely classical physics. You need quantum physics in order to understand how the jostling motions of particles produced this kind of shape.

The discussion will get a little bit more technical here, just briefly, for the enjoyment of those who want to see a little bit of the mathematics behind it. I stress that all of this can be understood in qualitative terms and you can ignore the mathematics if you don't want to look at it.

The most important point is that the wavelength at which the peak occurs is related to the temperature of the black body. Cool black bodies, such as those at 3,000°, still quite hot compared to anything in this room, peak at infrared wavelengths, about one micrometer, or 970 nanometers. A hotter black body peaks at a shorter wavelength. One at 5,000° peaks at a wavelength in the orange part of the spectrum (580 nanometers). Something like the Sun at about 6,000° Kelvin peaks in the blue-green part of the spectrum (489 nanometers). A hotter body still, 7,000° Kelvin, peaks way down in the blue to violet region (410 nanometers).

Notice that as temperature increases, the wavelength at which the peak occurs decreases. If you multiply those two numbers, you get a constant. This is an empirical relationship. The wavelength of the peak, λ_{max}, times the temperature (T) is a constant and that constant is roughly 2.9×10^6 nanometer Kelvin units—nanometer Kelvin, because wavelengths are given in nanometers and temperatures are given in Kelvin—or 2.9×10^7 angstrom Kelvin units.

$$\lambda_{max} T = 2.9 \times 10^6 \text{ n K} = 2.9 \times 10^7 \text{ Å K}$$

This relationship is known as Wien's law. Wien's law is one consequence of the more complicated mathematical expressions for the thermal Planck radiation coming from a perfect black body, which Planck derived near the beginning of this century.

If we look at a human holding a match, we see that the human emits radiation at infrared wavelengths. Our body temperatures are around 100° Fahrenheit. If you convert that to the Kelvin scale and use Wien's law, you find that we emit at infrared wavelengths. A match is somewhat hot and emits at somewhat shorter infrared wavelengths, but they are, nevertheless, infrared.

Here is an infrared view of a human holding a match. This is why infrared sensors can detect humans, tanks and other warm bodies at night. In fact, some animals have developed eyes that are primarily sensitive at infrared wavelengths because they need to see at night.

Our human eyes are sensitive at visible wavelengths. You might say, "According to the Planck curve of an object having a temperature of only 100° Fahrenheit, roughly 300° or so Kelvin, there shouldn't be any visible radiation. So, how then is it that we can see each other if we're not emitting any radiation of our own?"

My answer is of course that we reflect radiation. We reflect the light of the Sun and the Sun is sufficiently hot that it does produce visible light. We reflect the light from lamps in this room and they, too, are hot enough to produce visible light. We do not generate any visible light to speak of our own. We generate light at infrared wavelengths. Even though we are not perfect black bodies, just as the stars are not perfect black bodies; to a good first approximation, we are infrared emitters, and we are visible reflectors.

Let me show that then in a spectrum of a human. Brightness versus wavelength or color has two peaks. One is the thermal roughly black body emission that we produce. That peaks in the infrared part of the spectrum near a wavelength of 10 micrometers. Then there is the visible light, which peaks at around 5,000-6,000 angstroms (or 500-600 nanometers) and that is the reflective light from the sunlight or a bulb in the room, or whatever. When we see each other, we are seeing the reflected radiation from some other black body, or nearly black body. We are not seeing the black body radiation that we ourselves emit.

There's another interesting consequence of the Planck curves that are shown here. Not only do the hotter ones peak at a shorter wavelength, they are also higher than the curves corresponding to the colder bodies. Here's a body at 3,000° Kelvin. Another body at 4,000° Kelvin having the same surface area as the one at 3,000° has a peak, which is higher than that of the colder body; but, in fact, the curve is everywhere higher than that of the colder body. Again, per unit area, an object with a temperature of 5,000° has a peak that is higher and in fact everywhere the curve is higher.

This can be quantified by saying that the hotter bodies emit more total energy per second than the colder bodies. The area under that curve is bigger for a hotter body than it is for a colder body. A hotter body simply emits a lot more energy because the particles are jostling around way more than in a colder body. Mathematically, this is expressed as the Stefan-Boltzmann law.

Again, this is for those who are interested in this particular thing. If you're not interested, I'll get through it pretty quickly and we'll move on to more qualitative things.

Per unit of surface area, a hot opaque object, or a hot black body, emits much more energy per second than a cold black body. This is known as the Stefan-Boltzmann law. The energy emitted per unit area (cm^2) per second is proportional to the temperature to the fourth power. The constant of proportionality, the Greek small letter *sigma* (σ), is called the Stefan-Boltzmann constant.

Let's take as an example two stars of equal surface area, but one is twice as hot as the other—6,000° versus 3,000°. Per unit area, the hotter one emits more energy than the colder one. The amount by which it emits more energy is 2^4, because being twice as hot as the colder body and raising 2^4, you get 16 times as much energy emitted by that hot star compared with the cold star. This is for stars of equal area because per unit area, the hot one emits more energy.

Now suppose the star has a certain area and you'd like to know, what the total power or total luminosity emitted by that star is. The luminosity, or power of the star, is the total energy emitted per second by the entire object. To get the power of a black body or a star, multiply the surface area by the energy emitted per unit area per second. The area units cancel out and you simply have the energy emitted per second. So, luminosity (L) is surface area (S) times energy per second per unit area and that's then surface area times σT^4.

$$L = S\sigma T^4$$

For example, a star of radius R, the luminosity is the surface area of the star—$4\pi r^2$ (the surface area of a sphere)—multiplied by the amount emitted per unit area and that's σT^4. So you can calculate the power output of a star if you know its radius and you know its temperature. You can get the temperature from the wavelength at which the star's spectrum peaks. I'll tell you how we get the radius later on. This is how we calculate how powerful stars are.

Let's go back to more qualitative things. That was sort of a mathematical aside. Let's go now to the Sun, a typical star, and see what we can learn about the Sun, which is very nearby, and see whether we can apply it to distant stars. We'll see how distant stars might differ from the Sun in some ways and be similar to the Sun in other ways.

The Sun has this visible surface, which we call the photosphere, the region from which the photons appear to be generated. They're generated much farther in, of course, but they escape from the Sun at the region of the photosphere. There are other things such as sunspots, flares, the corona, prominences, the chromosphere and the solar wind. I'll talk about each of those in turn.

The Sun is about 109 times the diameter than the Earth, so it's much bigger than the Earth. About a million Earths could fit inside the Sun. The Sun is huge. Its mass is only 330,000 times that of the Earth, so its density (mass per unit volume) is somewhat lower than that of the Earth. That reflects the fact that the Sun is made mostly of compressed gases whereas the Earth consists of things like rocks, iron, and things like that.

The peak of the Sun's spectrum is at about 5,000 angstroms or so. The temperature of the Sun's photosphere is 5,800° Kelvin and the peak of the spectrum is at about 5,000 angstroms. That's in the greenish part of the spectrum, but as I mentioned before, the total physiological sensation that we get is that of white light, because the Sun does not emit only at green wavelengths. It emits at blue wavelengths and red wavelengths as well. The totality of all those wavelengths gives you white light. It is our definition of white light.

It is often the case that we see the Sun setting with a reddish or orange color. The Sun is often drawn with a yellow color. Those colors are not the real colors of the Sun. Most people are taught from Day One that the Sun is yellow. It actually is a blindingly white color. As we will see in the next lecture, when we consider the spectacular phenomenon of eclipses, this is very easily seen during an eclipse when the tiniest sliver of the Sun is still showing. You can look at it safely with you unaided eye and it's just a dazzling white color. It's not yellow at all.

We often call it yellow, orange or red because the only time its reasonably safe to look at the Sun is when it's setting down near the horizon. At that point the colors do appear yellowish, orange or red. That's because the sunlight is scattered and absorbed by gases and dust particles in our atmosphere.

Here's the sun at noon. Its sunlight is coming down through a layer of the atmosphere and a little bit of the light is absorbed and scattered. The nature of dust particles and molecules in our atmosphere is such that they tend to scatter and absorb violets, blues and greens more than yellows, oranges and reds. So the bluish colors tend to be preferentially scattered and absorbed leaving the yellows and reds behind.

When the Sun is high up in the sky, there's not much atmosphere to go through, so not much of the light is scattered out. As the Sun dips down toward the horizon getting closer to sunset, one can see that the total path through the atmosphere that the light traverses is much longer than when the Sun is high up in the sky at noon. So, there's much more of a chance for the sunlight to get scattered and absorbed. Since it the blues, greens and violets tend to be scattered and absorbed more than the reds and oranges, one tends to see a reddish-orange Sun at sunset. By the time the light reaches the observer, most of the blues are gone.

For a similar reason, if you look at the daytime sky away from the Sun, it appears blue, because the blues, violets and greens scatter better than the orange and red colors. The predominant color that we tend to see, due to the physiological response of our eye and the amount of scattering and so on, is blue.

Scattered light, from parts of the atmosphere away from the direction of the Sun, tend to be blue because that's what's scattered preferentially. Looking at the Sun, especially when it's near sunset, tends to give you the reds and the oranges because those are the only colors that directly traverse their way through the atmosphere and survive by the time they reach the observer. That's why sunsets are red and the blue sky is blue, but the Sun is intrinsically white.

What are these things called sunspots? What about these little granulations here in the photosphere of the Sun? It turns out that the bright and dark blotches that we see here in the photosphere are a manifestation of the Stefan-Boltzmann law, the fact that cooler bits of gas produce less energy than hotter bits of gas. Sunspots are cool regions of the photosphere and the little granules are hot regions. The regions surrounding the granules—you can barely see them here—are somewhat cooler regions. There are cool and hot regions on the Sun. The dark blotches simply emit less energy per unit area than the surrounding hotter regions. They appear darker in comparison with the hot surrounding regions; they're not really very dark intrinsically. If you took a sunspot, plucked it out of the sun, and just put it out into cold empty space alone, it would glow quite brightly. In fact, the sun's photosphere has a temperature of about 6,000° and sunspots are about 2,000° colder, so that's a temperature of 4,000°. That's hotter than a lot of stars. But in comparison with the hotter still photosphere, the sunspot looks dim and black. But if you plucked it out and put it out in space alone, you would see that it glows brightly.

The granules, then, are regions of hot gas upwelling from the interior of the Sun. They deposit their energy at the photosphere, the light gets radiated away and then the cooler gas comes back down to be heated up again in the Sun's hot interior. So it's like a fountain of gas, coming up, radiating its energy and then coming back down. The little granulations are the little tubes of gas coming up, radiating their energy and then on the outside, where they go back down, you tend to get a dark region around the tube. That's why you get this granulation.

A sunspot, a large region in which the sun looks dark, is a region where, in fact, the hot gas from the Sun's interior is prevented from coming up to the surface. There is a barrier there and that barrier is not a complete barrier, but it is an effective barrier. It turns out to be tangled magnetic fields. Charged particles have a hard time crossing through magnetic fields. Where you have tangled magnetic fields, the hot gases in the interior of the sun cannot come up and replenish the supply of hot gas at the photosphere. That region of a tangled magnetic field cools down. It radiates energy, becomes cooler and darker than its surroundings, and only later, when those magnetic fields disappear, do you have a chance to see hotter gas from the interior replenishing the supply and appearing bright again. Those are the sunspots.

Now let's look at some of the other phenomena related to the Sun. The sunspots can be enormous, especially during active stages of the Sun. The Sun sometimes goes through active stages. Here you can see a large pair of groups of sunspots. Here they are on the disk of the Sun. They're absolutely enormous. If you remember that 109 Earths could fit across the diameter of the Sun, you realize that these cool dark blotches are many Earth diameters in size. You can sometimes see them with the unaided eye, if you're looking through fog of the right thickness.

When the Sun is very active, it can produce these large gigantic sunspots. In some cases then, we can use those sunspots to measure the rotation rate of the Sun. Here is a sequence of photographs of the Sun taken every successive day and you can see this large pair of sunspots rotating across the face of the Sun. Every day, it gets farther towards the right as shown in this diagram. Then half a month later or so, it returns to the other side and you can see this progression once again.

This movement of the sunspots is due to the rotation of the Sun. It tells us that the Sun rotates roughly once per Earth-month, roughly thirty days. Near the equator, the rotation rate is faster than near the poles. It's maybe 25 days near the equator and 28 or 29 near the poles, even up to thirty. The Sun does not rotate as a solid body. The equator rotates faster than the poles. To a first approximation, the rotation period is roughly one month. The first indication we had of that was by looking at sunspots going across the face of the Sun.

The chromosphere of the Sun is a thin red layer just above the photosphere. It looks red because it's hot. It's at a temperature of 10,000° Kelvin, somewhat hotter than the photosphere of the Sun, and it glows red at this hot temperature primarily because hydrogen atoms have electrons jumping from the third to the second energy level. That is the so-called Balmer-α, or hydrogen-α, emission line of hydrogen that is roughly 10,000° in temperature. There are a lot of atoms there with electrons jumping from the third to the second energy level.

Why is the chromosphere hotter than the photosphere, when, in general, the interior of the Sun is hotter and it gets progressively colder as you go out? We're not totally sure, but we think that it is due to the mechanical heating of these granules of gas coming up; they're in motion, like this, and they heat mechanically the gases above them. Moreover, the magnetic fields sometimes dissipate energy and cause the chromosphere to become hot as well. We think it's a combination of the mechanical energy and magnetic energy.

Further out from the chromosphere is the corona. We will look at the corona much more in the next lecture when we discuss the glorious eclipses of the Sun. Suffice to say for now that the corona is a very hot, tenuous low-density outer atmosphere of the Sun and presumably of other stars as well. It has temperatures approaching 2,000,000° Kelvin; it's incredibly hot. We can tell that it's that hot because the atoms that we see in the corona are highly ionized as though they've hit each other with tremendous speeds and knocked all or most of the electrons off. It's much more highly ionized than the photospheric gases or the chromospheric gases.

Moreover, the corona emits X rays. Here you see an X ray image of the Sun. You can actually see in this image that the corona is a very irregular structure. It has bright spots, dense spots, hot spots, and darker spots. It too is probably heated by a combination of mechanical heating of these upwelling tubes of gas and magnetic energy. It is probably primarily heated by magnetic energy, although that's still a topic of great discussion.

The corona, though having a high temperature, does not have a large amount of heat content. That is there are not many particles out there. The ones that are there are moving really fast, but there are so few particles out there that if you placed yourself in the corona and suppose you blocked out the sun's photosphere, you would freeze in the corona. You would radiate energy, as a black body, faster than the collisions of this tenuous gas could replenish your supply. The corona, though having a high temperature, does not have large energy content because it is so tenuous.

There is also the solar wind, which is an extension of the corona. It is a bunch of charged particles, electrons and protons primarily, moving out from the Sun at speeds of up to 500 kilometers per second. A few hundred kilometers per second is typical. It's sort of an outer atmosphere of a star being blown away by ejection from the photosphere and by the pressure of radiation. Occasionally, during active stages, you get giant solar flares. You get enormous eruptions from the photosphere of the Sun and these really emit a huge amount of energy. Huge concentrations of energy emitted in a very small region of the Sun and they can reach temperatures of up to five million degrees. Probably, they're powered by some incredible concentration of magnetic energy that finally just dissipates in one fell swoop and produces a flare-like protrusion.

The so-called prominences are gentler. They seem to be loops of gas from the chromosphere or the upper part of the photosphere that follow the magnetic field lines in loopy structures like this. The ionized gas just goes along the magnetic field lines and then comes back down. These relatively mild eruptions are once again thought to be due to the sudden release of magnetic energy stored in the magnetic field of the Sun. The Sun is just permeated by magnetic fields.

Occasionally you can get gigantic solar prominences, such as the one shown in this picture. It extends over a distance roughly equal to one quarter of the Sun's diameter. That's many Earth diameters across. This is a powerful prominence, but still not as concentrated an ejection of energy as you get in a true solar flare.

All of these phenomena—sunspots, flares, prominences, and solar wind—appear to have a periodic behavior. If you plot the number of sunspots on the vertical axis versus time (a year) along the horizontal axis, you can see that sometimes there are very few sunspots. Correspondingly, there are very few solar flares and prominences, and things like that. At other times, there are large numbers of sunspots, flares and prominences. In some cases, the number of sunspots visible on the disk of the sun at any time might approach 200. At other times, it can be zero.

This appears to have a rough periodicity of around eleven years. This is called the solar sunspot cycle. It's an eleven-year cycle of ups and downs. We are on our way toward solar maximum right now, which will occur I think around the year 2001, plus or minus one year or so. We don't know exactly what causes this, but it all has to do with the magnetic field of the Sun. It looks like that of a bar magnet, a North Pole and a South Pole. To a first approximation, that's what the magnetic field of the Sun looks like and it's probably due to charged particles in the interior of the Sun sort of wandering around in coherent ways that produces a large scale magnetic field.

Then what happens to that field is that, although it might be roughly aligned with the north and South Poles of the Sun initially, the rotation of the Sun stretches out those fields. That's because the rotation viewed at the equator is faster than the rotation at the poles. Remember, the period at the equator is about 25 days and the period near the poles is 29 or 30 days. So, the equator rotates faster than the poles and the gases in the Sun drag the magnetic field along with them. The gases in the Sun are ionized. Again, magnetic fields have a hard time traveling through ionized gases or charged particles, so they just drag them with them. Instead of moving through the gases, they drag the gases with them.

The magnetic field lines are dragged along with the gas and after several rotations they kink up. In some places, they can break through the photosphere of the Sun as shown by these dotted curves right here, and a large amount of magnetic energy can be released. Where the field lines are kinked together, you have a large amount of magnetic energy. Where that energy can break through the photosphere—the dotted line means it's broken through—that's where, in fact, that energy can be released.

Solar flares tend to appear in these regions and sunspots tend to appear in these regions because these are regions of tangled intense magnetic fields, and they don't even allow hot gas to come up from the interior.

That's about it for the solar sunspot cycle, except a curious fact is that every time the sunspots appear and re-appear every eleven years, their polarity changes. In one cycle they might be north-south in the Northern Hemisphere and south-north in the Southern Hemisphere. The next eleven-year cycle it reverses. They're south-north up at the top and north-south at the north. The total sunspot cycle is twice eleven years. It's more like 22 years. The mystery is, what produces this? We don't exactly know what it is, but our Earth does something similar and it's some kind of a dynamo. Some kind of current or charge is moving around in the Sun to cause both the magnetic fields to form and to reverse themselves roughly every eleven years. The polarity reverses roughly every twenty-two years.

Lecture Eight
Lunar Phases and Glorious Eclipses

Scope:

Lunar phases are a consequence of changes in our viewing perspective of the Moon's illuminated hemisphere as the Moon orbits Earth over the course of about a month. The phases of Earth, as seen from the Moon, are like the lunar phases in reverse order. The Moon's visibility (time of day or night; location in the sky) is intimately linked with its phase. Lunar or solar eclipses occur when the Earth, Sun, and Moon are almost exactly aligned, but this does not occur each month due to the tilt between the Earth's orbital plane and that of the Moon. Total solar eclipses, among the most beautiful and thrilling celestial phenomena, provide information about the tenuous outer parts of the Sun. Though truly indescribable, we attempt to convey the excitement and awe of the phenomenon with photographs and words. Total solar eclipses were historically important in verifying a prediction of Einstein's general theory of relativity. Total lunar eclipses, of longer duration, are also visually stunning.

Objectives

Upon completion of this lecture, you should be able to:

1. Describe the phases of the Moon and what produces them.

2. Show that the visibility of the Moon (time; location in the sky) is related to its phase.

3. State the reason that lunar and solar eclipses don't occur each month.

4. Summarize what phenomena can be seen during the course of a total solar eclipse.

5. Explain how measurements during a total solar eclipse helped confirm Einstein's general theory of relativity.

6. Compare and contrast total solar and lunar eclipses.

7. Discuss why a fully eclipsed Moon is not completely dark, and appears orange/red.

Outline

I. All planets and moons in the Solar System shine at optical wavelengths only because they *reflect* light from the Sun; they are too cold to emit thermal visible radiation.

A. At any given time, only that half of a spherical object facing the Sun is illuminated.

B. At any given time, we see only the half of a spherical object that is facing us.

C. The sequence of lunar phases is a consequence of changes in our viewing perspective of the Moon's illuminated hemisphere as it orbits the Earth over ~1 month; see Figure 8-1

D. Popular misconceptions are that the lunar phases are caused by the Moon entering Earth's shadow, or by clouds in Earth's atmosphere, or by clouds on the Moon

E. Since the lunar phases are often misunderstood, they are described in detail here.

    1. Consider parallel rays of sunlight reaching the Earth-Moon system; see Figure 8-1. This diagram is crucial; if it is thoroughly digested, everything about the phases of the Moon can be reconstructed with minimal memorization.

        a. Note that the diagram remains the same even as the Earth-Moon system orbits the Sun; only the relative position of the Sun changes.

        b. For simplicity, assume we are observing from a location not too near the Earth's poles.

    2. When the Moon is between the Earth and the Sun, the Moon's illuminated half faces away from Earth; only the dark half is exposed to us.

        a. This is called "new moon."

        b. Being roughly aligned with the Sun, the new moon rises and sets approximately with the Sun, and crosses the meridian (its highest point in the sky) around noon.

c. Note that the Earth, Moon, and Sun are generally not exactly colinear (i.e., in a straight line) at this position because the Moon's orbital plane is tilted by about 5° with respect to Earth's orbital plane. Thus, a solar eclipse generally does not occur.

3. A few days later, when the Moon has moved eastward along its orbit to a new position (Fig. 8-1), the half that we see intersects the illuminated half by a small amount. Since the Moon is spherical, this illuminated part looks curved.

    a. This is called a "crescent moon."

    b. Since the visible illuminated region is growing larger each day, we call it a "waxing crescent."

    c. It rises around 9 am, crosses the meridian at ~3 pm, and sets in the west around 9 pm, a few hours after sunset. It is most prominent in the evening.

4. About a week after new moon, the Earth-Moon-Sun angle is 90° (a right angle). We see half of the illuminated side of the Moon.

    a. This is called the "quarter moon" (in fact, the "first quarter"); the Moon has moved through ¼ of its orbit, and we see one quarter of the Moon's entire surface.

    b. Some people call this the "half moon," since we see half of the side facing us, and it is more consistent with the "full moon" terminology discussed below.

    c. It rises around noon (6 hours later than at new moon), crosses the meridian at ~6 pm, and sets around midnight.

5. A few days later, we see more than half of the illuminated side of the Moon (Fig. 8-1).

    a. This is called the "gibbous moon" (in fact, "waxing gibbous" since the illuminated region grows larger each day).

    b. It rises around 3 pm, crosses the meridian at ~9 pm, and sets around 3 am.

6. About two weeks after new moon, the Earth is between the Moon and the Sun; the Moon is opposite the Sun in the sky. The Moon's illuminated side faces Earth, and we therefore see all of it.

a. This is called the "full moon," since the Moon appears fully lit up, even though we actually see only half of it (and "half moon" would be more consistent with the "quarter moon" terminology used earlier).

b. It rises at sunset, crosses the meridian around midnight, and sets at sunrise.

c. As with the new moon, note that the Moon, Earth, and Sun are usually not exactly colinear at this position due to the 5° tilt of the Moon's orbital plane. Thus, a lunar eclipse generally does not occur.

7. From Figure 8-1, it is easy to see that the Moon subsequently goes through the waning gibbous, third quarter, and waning crescent phases before reaching new moon once again.

8. One can deduce from the above discussion that the Moon rises (and sets) an average of about 50 minutes later each day, due to its eastward motion of ~12°. Over the course of its orbit (about 29.5 days), the total necessarily adds up to 24 hours (1 day).

F. To reproduce the lunar phases yourself, put a bright lightbulb at one end of a room, and hold a small ball between your head and the bulb. You will see a "new moon." As you move the ball around your head, other phases will become apparent.

G. Note that the Moon can often be seen during the day. For example, the first quarter moon is up and easily visible in the afternoon.

H. When the Moon is in its crescent phase, its "dark side" is sometimes easily visible.

1. This phenomenon is called "earthshine."

2. From the Moon's perspective, the Earth is nearly fully illuminated—it is in its gibbous phase.

3. Light reflected by the Earth reaches the Moon and is reflected back toward the Earth; thus, the Moon's dark side is indirectly illuminated.

4. During the quarter and gibbous lunar phases, earthshine is more difficult to see.

a. A smaller portion of the illuminated Earth is visible from the Moon, so there is less reflected light.

      b. The visible illuminated portion of the Moon is larger and brighter, and the glare drowns out the fainter earthshine.

I. The Moon looks larger when it is near the horizon than when it is high in the sky.

    1. This is just an illusion; it is easier to compare the Moon's angular size with that of known objects (distant trees, buildings, etc.) when it is rising or setting.

    2. The illusion persists even when the Moon rises over the ocean, probably because our brains still remember how big objects appear near the horizon.

    3. The Moon actually has a *smaller* angular diameter when near the horizon, because we view it from a distance of one Earth radius farther than when it is almost overhead.

II. Solar eclipses occur when the Moon is exactly, or almost exactly, between the Earth and the Sun.

    A. The Moon casts a shadow in space, but this shadow can intersect Earth only if the alignment is very good.

      1. Because of the 5° tilt between the Moon's orbital plane around the Earth, and the Earth's orbital plane around the Sun, the new moon's shadow generally misses the Earth.

      2. These two inclined planes intersect in a line; the Sun, Moon, and Earth can therefore be roughly colinear during two intervals per year, separated by six months.

      3. These "eclipse seasons" do not always yield an eclipse, however, since the Moon must be in the right part of its orbit when the potential for alignment exists.

    B. Although the Sun's physical diameter is about 390 times the Moon's diameter, the Sun is also about 390 times farther from Earth than the Moon is.

      1. Thus, the Sun and the Moon subtend (cover) roughly the same angle in the sky: $\frac{1}{2}°$.

      2. This cosmic coincidence allows us to see total solar eclipses: the Moon's shadow reaches the Earth.

      3. The solar chromosphere and photosphere are visible only during complete (or very nearly complete) totality because they are much fainter than the sunlit sky.

4. As the Moon orbits the Earth, the location at which totality is seen sweeps across the Earth from west to east along a narrow path (typically 100 to 200 km wide).

5. At locations adjacent to this path, a partially eclipsed Sun is observed; part of the Moon blocks part of the Sun's photosphere. The fraction covered decreases with increasing distance from the path of totality.

6. Although the partial phases span 2 to 3 hours, totality at a given location lasts only a few minutes; very rarely it lasts over 5 minutes, but never in excess of 7.3 minutes.

   a. The duration depends primarily on the relative angular sizes of the Sun and Moon. These vary from one eclipse to another because both the Earth's orbit and the Moon's orbit are elliptical.

   b. A long eclipse occurs when the Moon is closer to Earth than average, because it looks large relative to the Sun. It also helps if the Sun is farther from Earth than average, so that it looks smaller.

7. A total solar eclipse occurs somewhere on Earth every 1.5 years, on average.

8. At a given location, totality is seen roughly every 360 years, on average. Thus, one must travel to have a good chance of experiencing totality! The next total solar eclipse visible from parts of North America will occur on 21 August 2017.

C. During a total solar eclipse, the following phenomena are seen.

   1. First contact: the moment the Moon begins to cover the Sun's photosphere.

   2. Partial phases: progressively more of the Sun is covered. The sky doesn't darken appreciably until well over half of the photosphere is blocked.

   3. "Shadow bands": when only a thin sliver of the photosphere is uncovered, low-contrast bands of light are sometimes seen shimmering across the ground. They are produced by inhomogeneities in Earth's atmosphere. A useful analogy is the bands seen at the bottom of a swimming pool, which are produced by surface ripples.

   4. The shadow of the Moon looms in the west, approaching quickly.

5. "Baily's beads": only a small part of the photosphere is uncovered, and small bits can shine through valleys at the Moon's edge, creating a few short-lived beads of sunlight. The sky darkens rapidly, and the air temperature drops.

6. "Diamond ring": can be considered the last Baily's bead. Only a tiny fraction of the photosphere is uncovered. The chromosphere and inner corona become visible, and form a ring around the dark Moon. The much brighter photosphere looks like a glistening white diamond for a few seconds. Often prominences are visible as well. The final darkening of the sky is very rapid and dramatic.

7. Totality: all of the Sun's photosphere is covered. The sky is relatively dark (though somewhat brighter than on a night of full moon), and the full corona appears, usually with beautiful and complex structure. Large prominences can be seen, as well as the chromosphere near the beginning and end of totality. Bright stars and planets are visible.

8. After totality ends, the above sequence is seen in reverse: there is another diamond ring, perhaps some Baily's beads, the receding shadow of the Moon, shadow bands, and the full set of partial phases.

9. The entire phenomenon of a total solar eclipse is indescribably beautiful. Most people who have seen one found it to be a very moving experience. Photographs and words simply do not convey the drama, beauty, and thrill of a total solar eclipse: it must be witnessed in person!

D. The partially eclipsed Sun must not be viewed directly; a special dark filter should be used.

1. An indirect way of viewing the partial phases is with a "pinhole camera": punch a small hole in some cardboard, and project an image of the Sun onto the ground, in the shadow of the cardboard.

2. Holes between leaves in trees can form natural pinhole cameras: many crescent Suns are seen on the ground!

E. Contrary to popular belief, the totally eclipsed Sun is perfectly safe to view directly with the unaided eye, binoculars, or a telescope.

1. However, if even a tiny part of the photosphere is uncovered, binoculars or telescopes should *not* be used: they collect enough light to quickly damage the retina.
2. The diamond ring is safe to observe for a few seconds with the unaided eye, but not with binoculars or telescopes.

F. If the Moon is farther from Earth than average, and the Sun is closer than average (e.g., in January), the Moon's angular diameter is somewhat smaller than that of the photosphere.
   1. The Sun is not completely eclipsed. Instead, an annulus of the photosphere surrounds the dark Moon.
   2. Such an *annular eclipse* is only a special case of a partial solar eclipse, but a memorable one.

III. Measurements during solar eclipses provided the first observational confirmation of a prediction made by Albert Einstein with his general theory of relativity.

A. This theory, published in 1916, postulates that mass warps space and time, producing the phenomenon we call gravity.
   1. Particles follow their natural paths through curved space-time; indeed, this is why planets orbit the Sun.
   2. The theory predicts that light should also follow a curved path.

B. Light passing close to the edge of the Sun should bend, but only a little because the Sun's mass is small. The deflection decreases with increasing angular distance from the Sun.
   1. This effect seems impossible to measure, since stars are invisible when the Sun is up!
   2. During a total solar eclipse, however, bright stars are visible, and their apparent positions can be measured.
   3. These apparent positions can be compared with the "true" positions, as measured in a photograph obtained during a time of year when those stars up at night.
   4. The observations are difficult: only stars adjacent to the edge of the Sun undergo the full deflection, but bright stars are rare, and the inner corona overwhelms faint stars.
   5. Success was first achieved by Arthur Eddington during a total solar eclipse in 1919: the shift of stars at the edge of the Sun was 1.7 seconds of arc, as predicted by the theory.

6. News of the confirmation made Einstein an instant celebrity; before this he was still obscure, at least to the lay public.
7. Measurements during subsequent eclipses were used to confirm the predicted bending.

IV. Lunar eclipses occur when the Earth is exactly, or almost exactly, between the Sun and the Moon.

A. Earth casts a shadow in space, but this shadow intersects the Moon only if the alignment is very good. This can happen during two "eclipse seasons" per year, as for solar eclipses.
1. When part (or all) of the Moon is immersed in the Earth's shadow, we have a partial (or total) lunar eclipse.
2. From the Moon's perspective, the Earth blocks all of the Sun's photosphere during a total lunar eclipse.
3. Since the Earth's shadow is nearly three times the size of the Moon at the Moon's distance from Earth, a total lunar eclipse lasts about an hour. It is a leisurely affair compared with a total solar eclipse!
4. Note that a total lunar eclipse is visible from the entire dark hemisphere of Earth. From any given location of Earth, total lunar eclipses are therefore much more common than total solar eclipses, even though they occur with about the same intrinsic frequency.

B. The Moon is not completely dark during a total lunar eclipse.
1. The Earth's atmosphere refracts (bends) some of the sunlight toward the Moon.
2. Blue and green photons are preferentially absorbed and scattered, leaving predominantly orange and red light to pass through. This is the same effect that we see during sunset.
3. Thus, the fully eclipsed Moon generally looks reddish-orange.
4. If the Moon goes through the central part of the Earth's shadow, or if there is a large amount of dust or smoke in the atmosphere, the eclipse looks darker than usual.

Essential Reading:

Harris, J., and Talcott, R. *Chasing the Shadow: An Observer's Guide to Eclipses*. Kalmbach Pub., 1994.

Littmann, M., and Willcox, K. *Totality: Eclipses of the Sun*. Univ. Hawaii Press, 1991.

Long, K. *The Moon Book*. Johnson Pub., 1988.

Questions to Consider:

1. What would be the phase of the Earth, as seen from the Moon at each lunar phase?

2. During a total lunar eclipse, what would someone on the Moon see when looking toward the Sun?

3. How is it possible that a given solar eclipse can sometimes be both total and annular? (That is, along part of the central eclipse path the photosphere is entirely hidden, but along other parts a thin annulus is visible.)

Figure 8-1

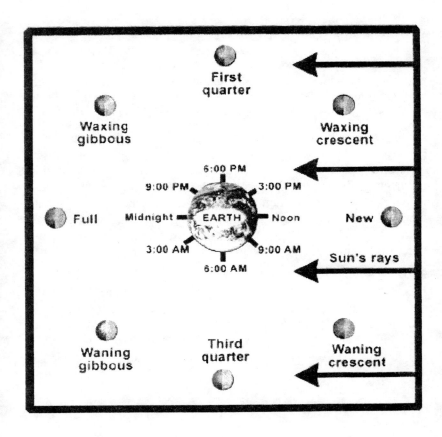

Lecture Eight—Transcript
Lunar Phases and Glorious Eclipses

In the previous lecture, we briefly discussed the Sun and the stars, which are so hot inside that they generate visible light through the jiggling of charged particles in their interiors. The planets, and the moons of the planets, are too cold to generate visible light. Their particles don't move around sufficiently quickly to produce visible electromagnetic radiation. They radiate at infrared wavelengths.

We can see them at visible wavelengths only by the light that they reflect from the Sun. For example, if the Sun is over here and my head is the Earth, the Moon, as it's orbiting the Earth, presents different faces towards me. The illuminated face of the Moon might not necessarily be the same face that I see. For example, if the Moon is over here and the illuminated face is this one, the illuminated hemisphere which is the hemisphere facing the Sun, I won't see that hemisphere and I won't see the Moon. However, if the Moon is over here, the illuminated hemisphere is partially visible by me from the Earth. I can see a partially lit Moon.

It is this phenomenon, the orbit of the Moon around the Earth and the changing aspect of the illuminated hemisphere that gives rise to the observed phases of the Moon. Let's review the phases of the Moon. On your television screen, you see nothing right now. That would be the new moon. You cannot see the new moon when it's at this phase. The crescent moon is partly lit up from our perspective. The so-called first-quarter moon is somewhat later in time than the crescent moon and now we see half of the lit up hemisphere. The gibbous moon is when the hemisphere is even more lit up. Finally, the full moon is when we see the fully lit hemisphere. The dark hemisphere of the Moon is hidden from our view at this phase.

Proceeding onwards in the lunar month, we have the waning gibbous moon, then the so-called third-quarter moon and finally the crescent moon, before moving back to new moon, which is no moon at all.

The different geometry of the Moon relative to the sun and the Earth causes this change in the phases of the Moon and is often misunderstood by people. A lot of people think that clouds on the Moon, or clouds in the Earth's atmosphere, or clouds in the Earth's atmosphere cause the phases of the Moon; but it's caused by a changing geometrical relationship among the Earth, which is the observer, and the Moon and the Sun. We only see that part of the Moon, which is illuminated. The Moon is only illuminated on half of its surface at any given time. The hemisphere that faces the Sun is the illuminated hemisphere.

Let me demonstrate this perhaps more clearly with the following model. We have here the Sun. Let's ignore Venus for the time being. Here is the Earth and the Moon. When the Moon is between the Earth and the Sun, its illuminated hemisphere is hidden from view. We here on Earth do not see the illuminated hemisphere; instead we see no moon at all or the new moon.

Farther in time like this, the Moon is illuminated still by the Sun. One hemisphere is still illuminated, but we only see half of that illuminated hemisphere. Later, we can see the fully illuminated hemisphere and that would be the full moon. Still later, we see again only half of the illuminated hemisphere. This is the illuminated hemisphere, but this is the hemisphere we see; only half of the illuminated hemisphere is visible.

When half of the illuminated hemisphere is visible, we call that the quarter-moon phase. One might more reasonably call it the half-moon. After all, when we see the fully illuminated hemisphere, we call that the full moon, so why not call the half-illuminated hemisphere the half moon? By tradition, astronomers call it the quarter-moon because the Moon is either one quarter of the way around the Earth or three quarters of the way around the Earth in its monthly orbit.

When it's halfway around the Earth, we call it full moon rather than the half moon. There's a slight inconsistency there. It's just something that we have to accept. First quarter is a half-lit moon; the full moon is a fully lit moon. If the terminology were completely consistent, we should call that the half moon, but we don't.

The point is that the illuminated face is not the face we see. It is this changing geometry that leads to the observed phases of the Moon.

You might think that at this position here that the Moon will always fall in the Earth's shadow. In this model, in fact, the Moon does fall inside the Earth's shadow when the geometry is such that the three bodies are aligned. That would be a lunar eclipse. Similarly, when the Moon is between the Earth and the Sun, the Moon's shadow falls on the Earth and that would be then a solar eclipse, but that doesn't happen every month. You can't see that very well in this model because this is not a correctly proportioned scale model. We can't make a correctly proportioned scale model that would fit in this room because the Sun is 109 times bigger than the Earth, and the distance between the Sun and the Earth-Moon system is far greater than the distance between the Earth and the Moon. So the relative sizes and distances are simply wrong in this model and we can't do any better in any reasonably sized room.

It looks like the Earth's shadow always blocks the Moon at full moon and that the Moon's shadow always falls on the Earth at new moon, but that is not actually the case. It's not the case because the Moon's orbit around the Earth is tilted by about 5° relative to the Earth-Sun plane. Let me move the model over here to make it easier. Normally what happens is that the Moon is above the Earth-Sun plane so its shadow misses the Earth at new moon or at the full-moon phase. The Earth's shadow misses the Moon, so at full moon you don't always get an eclipse.

At certain times of the year like this, let me try that again keeping the orientation of the plane the same; when the configuration is like this, then the Moon can, in fact, be along the same line as the Earth and the Sun. Similarly, over here, it can be along the same line as the Earth and Sun. You do get eclipses of the Moon and the Sun at certain times of the year, but not always.

You can't see it, but here you could see an eclipse because there's a chance for the Moon to be directly between the Earth and the Sun, or for the Moon to be directly on the opposite side of the Earth opposite to the Sun. So, you can get eclipses at certain times of the year.

You won't always get an eclipse when you have this kind of configuration, because the Moon has to be at the proper position at the proper time. If, when the orbits are oriented in this way, the Moon happens to be over here, then again you don't have a co-linear configuration, so you won't get an eclipse. There are potentially two seasons in the year when eclipses can occur, but they don't always occur during those seasons.

Those are the lunar phases. They're not due to clouds. They're not due to the Earth's shadow. They're simply due to the changing orientation and geometry among the Sun, the Earth and the Moon.

Let's now look at the relationship between the phases of the Moon and the times at which you can see the Moon. In the diagram on your television screen, you can see that in the configuration when we have a new moon, the Sun's rays are coming from the right, illuminating one hemisphere of the Moon. That is not the hemisphere to which we are exposed, so we just see the dark hemisphere.

The Sun is overhead or at its highest point in the sky at noon, as seen by an observer here at point H. The Moon as well would be overhead or at its highest position at that same time (noon), because the Moon and the Sun are aligned during new moon. That means the new moon tracks the Sun very closely and sets when the Sun sets and rises when the Sun rises. The new moon rises and sets exactly with the Sun.

Let's now consider the crescent moon. The Sun's rays, once again, are coming in from the right, illuminating the hemisphere that faces the Sun. We now, from Earth, can see part of that illuminated hemisphere. This little section right here falls within the face that we can see. Projected onto a sphere, that causes the crescent shape. You'll notice that this crescent moon is overhead at 3:00 p.m. in the afternoon. This person is standing there and looking straight up; if it's not straight up, it is at least the highest point in the sky to which the Moon gets. That highest point occurs around 3:00 p.m. That means that the crescent moon will set later than the Sun by three or four hours, so the evening skies sometimes have a crescent moon.

When we go to the first quarter moon, one can see it's visible overhead at about 6:00 p.m. You see the first quarter because that's only the half of the illuminated face that is visible. It sets about six hours after the Sun sets.

Moving on to the full moon, it's opposite the Sun, so it rises as the Sun sets. The full moon always rises roughly at sunset, so you can see that the phases of the Moon are related to the sunset and sunrise times. You will never see a full moon in the direction or near the direction of the Sun because the geometry is wrong.

It's interesting to consider what an observer on the Moon would see when looking back towards the Earth. Here we can see the phenomenon known as earthshine. The normally dark portion of the Moon is faintly visible in this photograph. That's because, from the perspective of an observer on the Moon, the Earth is nearly fully lit at this phase. An observer on the Moon sees a gibbous Earth because the Sun is over here and the Moon is over here. An observer on the Moon sees a nearly fully lit Earth. The light from Earth is reflecting back towards the Moon, hitting the Moon's surface, and reflecting back towards us. That is the phenomenon of earthshine. As the phase of the Moon gets bigger towards quarter moon, not only is the glare from the illuminated face of the Moon greater, but also the amount of light reflected from the Earth is smaller. For those two reasons the degree of earthshine decreases as the lunar phase increases towards first quarter and full moon.

The rising Moon and the rising Sun often look very big and people ask the question, "Is the rising Moon really bigger than the Moon when it's high up in the sky?" It turns out it's not, that's just an illusion. It's thought to be due to the fact that when the Moon is rising, there are reference points like trees and buildings with which your brain can compare the size of the Moon, whereas when it's high up in the sky, those reference points are not around, so the Moon looks small. You might think that that doesn't really work because the full moon looks big even when it's rising over the ocean, but your brain remembers when looking at any horizon the rough sizes of buildings and trees, and things like that. The phenomenon persists that the Moon and the Sun look big when they're near the horizon.

In fact, if anything, they're smaller when they're near the horizon. You can see that from this diagram here. The Sun's rays are coming in from the right. If you see the full moon when it's rising, you can see it, say, at 6:00 p.m. looking in this direction. You're actually farther from the Moon, at this position, than when you see the full moon overhead at midnight. At midnight, you're one Earth radius closer to the full moon than you are when you view the full moon when it's rising. So, if anything, you're closer to the Moon when it's overhead, and the Moon should appear bigger when it's overhead, not smaller. The psychological illusion of the Moon rising relative to trees and buildings and the horizon simply fools our brain into thinking that the Moon looks bigger when it's rising, but it's not really bigger when it's rising.

Now I want to consider eclipses of the Sun and the Moon. These are really glorious phenomena. Eclipses of the Sun are among the most incredible sights I've ever seen. It's not just the beauty of the solar corona coming out. It's the whole phenomenon of the Sun being sort of eaten alive. You can imagine how the ancients must have felt before they understood what causes the Sun to go away occasionally like this. They thought that maybe the Sun is going away permanently and terrible disasters are coming to Earth. In fact, all sorts of people have apparently done great damage to themselves when they thought that the world was coming to an end during an eclipse.

It's a beautiful phenomenon. You can see the darkening sky and feel the temperatures falling. You observe subtle changes in lighting patterns and can watch how animals behave; they do strange things. The whole experience is something that is difficult to describe to those who haven't seen it. Anyone who has seen an eclipse sounds nutty when describing the event to someone who has not been so initiated. It's like no other feeling that I know of. Comparable feelings are the birth of a baby, or a first kiss, or something like that, but they're all different in their own way. It's an indescribable experience and I can only say that you should see one if you can.

A lunar eclipse is also a beautiful phenomenon. It doesn't have quite the same intensity of a solar eclipse because it lasts for about an hour, whereas a total solar eclipse lasts for only a few minutes so you don't have much time to soak in everything. A lunar eclipse is quite pretty to view, in a leisurely way.

Let's look at the geometry of eclipses in a bit more detail than I did a few minutes ago. During a solar eclipse, the Moon's shadow hits the Earth. From the perspective of someone on Earth, the Moon's angular size is the same as that of the Sun, so it can block the Sun completely.

Let me show this with a little demonstration. This quarter will be the moon and this plate is the Sun. If I put the quarter at a certain distance from my eye, I can just barely block the plate, the Sun. The quarter is about five times smaller in size than the plate is, so I have to bring it five times closer to my eye than the plate in order to make the angular sizes seem the same. If I have it too close, then it covers more than the plate. If I have it too far away, the moon or the quarter seems too small, so it does not completely cover the plate.

I have to have it at precisely the right distance and it appears to be just an accident of nature that the Moon is 390 times smaller in physical diameter than the Sun but also 390 times closer to us than the Sun. It is because of this accident of nature that we can see solar eclipses. Notice that only a small portion of the Earth will see this particular geometry. If you're slightly away from the place where the cone intersects the Earth, part of the Sun will be visible, but the Moon will block part of it. You will see only a partial eclipse in this particular location. That is a picture of a partial eclipse. They're kind of fun to watch but you never see the corona, chromosphere or the prominences. You just see a slightly diminished amount of light with a chunk taken out of part of the Sun. It's a fun thing to watch but it's not really very exciting. It's just sort of an interesting curiosity.

Here you can see the path of a total solar eclipse that occurred in 1991. The paths in totality are only a couple of hundred kilometers wide, so you have to be at the right place at the right time. Away from the path of totality, you see partial eclipses of differing depth or magnitude. Close to the line of totality, you get quite a deep partial eclipse with only a thin crescent showing. Progressively farther from the path of totality, you see a progressively less eclipsed Sun until, far from the path of totality; you don't see any eclipse at all because the Moon is not projected towards the Sun in any way from this location on Earth.

Here, again, you can see the geometry from more of a 3-D perspective. The Moon's shadow hits only a small location of the Earth but that location sweeps across the Earth as the Moon orbits the Earth. Initially, when the Moon is over here, say, the projection of the Moon's shadow onto the Earth occurs more to the west of what's shown in this diagram. Later, as the Moon moves farther over in its orbit, a place on Earth east of the one you see in this diagram experiences a total solar eclipse. The eclipse paths on Earth are narrow swaths, usually curved because the projection of the Moon's motion onto the curved surface of the Earth is a curved path. You have to be in the right place at the right time in order to see an eclipse.

An eclipse is visible roughly once every 360 years from any given location on the Earth, so you generally have to make an effort to go see an eclipse. You can't just stand around waiting for one to come to you. You have to go and actively seek eclipses out, unless you happen to be very lucky. In a few places on Earth, like the middle of the Atlantic Ocean, there were two eclipses spaced not too far apart in time. Indonesia seems to have received a fairly good share of eclipses. But generally, a given point will not experience an eclipse for several hundred years.

Should you go see one? Absolutely. As I said, people kind of go nutty and it's perhaps hard to see in this diagram, but here's a fellow in India who decided to get a haircut in the shape of an eclipse because he was so excited to see one.

The phenomenon is beautiful to watch. Here is a picture using multiple exposures to show the progression of an eclipse from beginning to end. The Sun is initially un-eclipsed. Then the crescent becomes smaller and smaller until we have a fully eclipsed Sun, and then the phenomenon unfolds in reverse after the totality ends. The whole thing lasts a few hours, but totality itself only lasts a couple of minutes.

Here is the partially eclipsed Sun again and, as the Moon crosses the Sun's disk, you see progressively less of it, progressively less light. Initially, your eye balances for the gradually decreasing amount of sunlight. Our eyes experience physiological changes and the pupils can dilate as the Sun's intensity goes down. In the last few moments, when only a tiny sliver of the Sun is seen, the darkening effect is dramatic. If you look toward the west, you can actually see the approaching shadow of the Moon coming towards you. It's like a big column coming towards you. The column of doom, you might think. Except now with science and geometry, we understand that this is just a fleeting column and it is not a column of doom at all. It's a column of glory.

When the Moon nearly fully covers the sun's photosphere, little bits of the photosphere can shine through valleys on the Moon. The Moon's limb, or edge, is not perfectly smooth. There are craters, mountain ranges and valleys, and little bits of the photosphere can shine through these valleys. That produces a phenomenon known as Baily's beads.

When the last tiny bit of the photosphere is showing, you have the diamond ring effect. At this point, so little of the photosphere is showing that the inner parts of the corona start to become visible. The corona is very faint and tenuous, but the innermost parts are the brightest. When only a tiny bit of the photosphere is showing, you can begin to see those inner parts of the corona. This is a much over-exposed picture of a tiny bit of the photosphere that's still showing. It gives rise to a phenomenon called the diamond ring effect.

Here is a close-up of the diamond ring. To the right of the diamond, you can see one of the prominences, which I discussed in the last lecture.

Here are some more prominences. You can actually see in this photograph a little bit of the chromosphere, this thin layer of hot glowing hydrogen gas that glows with sort of a red color.

Finally, we have the fully eclipsed Sun. These differ from one eclipse to another, the structure of the corona changes. Sometimes it's more symmetric. Sometimes you have streamers going out along the equator of the Sun. It's just a glorious thing to see. No photograph does justice to the totally eclipsed Sun because there are many variations in the brightness of the corona. Your eye can see both the bright parts and the faint parts simultaneously because it's very good at doing that, whereas a photographic emulsion sees only black and white, with shades of gray and white being difficult to discern.

Here's a more symmetric corona from a different eclipse. It's fun to look at the colors of the atmosphere during the time of totality. A few hundred miles away, or even a hundred or two hundred miles away, observers are seeing nearly a fully eclipsed sun, but not a totally eclipsed sun. Light from those locations is filtering towards us and the atmosphere resembles that seen during twilight, or during the time of the sunset normally on Earth. You have only a tiny bit of the Sun filtering through a relatively large amount of the atmosphere. You get these twilight colors surrounding you in all directions. In a 360° circle, you see these twilight colors from light streaming towards you from regions that are experiencing a nearly fully eclipsed Sun but not a totally eclipsed Sun. That's fun to look at. Planets come out. Stars come out. It's just a neat thing to view.

The progression of these phases takes one or two hours, maybe three hours maximum, and gives a lot of time for viewing the partially eclipsed Sun as the intensity really goes up near the time of totality. My first eclipse was in February 1979 in Oregon, where the skies were totally cloudy up until a few minutes before the eclipse. Occasionally the partially eclipsed Sun would peak through the clouds but we were kind of depressed for a while. In fact, it was raining for part of the time.

As the eclipse progressed, and the crescent became smaller and smaller, the clouds almost magically cleared away. Actually, we think, it wasn't completely a coincidence because with the diminishing heating of the Earth's atmosphere, the clouds can actually dissipate. Sometimes, the heating of the atmosphere and the churning of the atmospheric layers produce clouds. I don't think it was entirely a coincidence that the clouds disappeared. Just before the moment of totality, the last cloud cleared away from the Sun, leaving a nice diamond ring and a beautifully clear totality. This was my first total eclipse of the Sun and I became hooked at that stage. I am now an addict and travel to far corners of the world to see solar eclipses. It's a fun thing to do.

Contrary to popular belief, total eclipses of the Sun are perfectly safe to view with your unaided eye, or even through a telescope or with binoculars. The corona is very faint; it has very little light at all. In fact, it's roughly the brightness of, maybe, a few times the full moon, or something like that. You know that it's safe to look at the Moon when it's full.

You can even use binoculars or a telescope to look at the totally eclipsed phases, but you have to be extraordinarily careful to remove all optical aids before totality ends. This is extremely important to stress. Suppose only one percent of the photosphere is showing but you're viewing it through binoculars, which have a much larger collecting area than the pupil of your eye. You will collect far more light from the Sun than your eye normally would. Even for such small binoculars, you collect five to six times as much light from the Sun as a completely un-eclipsed Sun. You're concentrating that light on a very small part of your retina, because only a tiny amount of the photosphere is showing. Therefore, you're concentrating a large amount of light onto a small area of your retina, and that can cause permanent damage. It's important to remove all optical aids before totality ends. Usually, someone is watching the clock to warn people when totality is about to end.

You can watch the partial phases through several techniques. For example, projecting the Sun's light through a telescope gives a view of the crescent on a piece of cardboard underneath the telescope. Or you can make a little pinhole camera. Just punch a hole through a piece of cardboard and project the Sun's image onto another piece of cardboard. You will get the projection of what you might think is the circular shape of the hole, but that's not true. You'll actually get a crescent shape because you form a complete image of the sun as the rays are passing through that hole. Nature provides us with lots of fun holes. These are crescent moons produced by holes in leaves of a tree or the spaces between the leaves of a tree. Those spaces are generally not round, so that they're certainly generally not crescent shaped; you are truly seeing images of the crescent sun when you look at the sunlight filtering through holes of arbitrary shape between leaves in a tree. That's kind of a fun thing to do.

You can also use blocking lenses to view the Sun safely during the partial phases. You can use dark welder's glass. Shade number 14 is good. Then the Sun is perfectly safe to view in its crescent phase. But you don't want to look at it with your unaided eye and certainly not with any sort of binoculars or a telescope.

These partial phases are much more often visible than totality. You can go quite far off from the path of totality and still see a partially eclipsed Sun, so those are much more common. You can generally see one once or twice a year, whereas totality occurs somewhere on Earth roughly every 1.5 years. But you have to travel to that location to actually see totality.

Occasionally, you don't see a totally eclipsed Sun because the Moon's orbit around the Earth is elliptical; it's not a circle. An ellipse is the shape that you get when you cut a cone with a plane tilted a little bit relative to the cone. Sometimes the Moon is farther from the Earth than average and sometimes it's closer than average. When it's farther than average, it appears smaller. When it's closer than average, it appears bigger. Here are two pictures of the Moon taken with the same camera, one when the Moon was farther than average from Earth and one when it was closer than average. When it's farther than average, it does not completely eclipse the Sun.

Moreover, the Earth's orbit around the Sun is slightly elliptical, so the Sun's angular size changes a little bit too. When we are closer than average to the Sun, the Sun appears slightly bigger. That accentuates the difference between the angular sizes of the Sun and the Moon. This leads to the phenomenon known as the annular eclipse. It's a special case of a partial eclipse. It is fun to watch and it can be strikingly beautiful such as in this shot of the annular eclipse near sunset.

Eclipses, besides being fun and glorious to watch—an amazing experience that no one should miss in their lives—also have great scientific value. The corona is so tenuous and faint that it really cannot be seen from the ground during times other than a total eclipse. That's because Earth's atmosphere scatters the sunlight and makes the sky too bright in comparison with the corona, so you cannot see the corona. It's even very hard to see the chromosphere. You can only do it with special equipment. Prominences can be seen with special equipment. Again, all of these phenomena are best seen during an eclipse.

Perhaps the most famous use of an eclipse has been to test Einstein's theory of general relativity, which postulates that gravity is actually a curvature of space and time. I will discuss this much more extensively when I discuss black holes and collapsed objects like neutron stars. Einstein predicts that space is curved and that curvature of space actually bends the light rays from stars so that their apparent positions as seen from the Earth differ from their true positions that would be seen if the Sun were absent.

In this diagram I show the true positions of two stars. That is, the positions in the sky that would be seen by an observer on Earth if the Sun were not present. This star would be here, and this other star would be there in the sky. When the Sun is present, it warps space-time around it. In that case, a light ray initially headed in this direction from the star will bend, due to the gravity of the Sun and hit an observer on Earth. An observer on Earth cannot measure that bending in real time. When you're looking at a photon that's coming towards you, you don't know what that photon did along the way towards you. All you know is the incoming direction.

The projected direction of that star is up here, slightly displaced from the true position of the star, and similarly for the other star. The closer a star is to the apparent limb of the Sun, the greater is this bending. A star way up here on the screen whose light would normally come down towards you from this direction is not bent very much by the Sun's gravity because the curvature is greatest very close to the Sun.

When we look at this diagram here, you can see that a star's apparent position is shifted the most when it's close to the Sun. Stars whose true positions are slightly farther from the Sun are shifted less.

It's difficult to measure this effect and confirm Einstein's prediction because the Sun is up during the day and the reflected light, the scattered light from the atmosphere, blocks out all the stars. They're there but you can't seem them. They're there all the time but you can't see them.

However, you can see at least the brightest stars during a total solar eclipse. The sky is dark enough for you to be able to see the brightest stars. Sir Arthur Eddington did this experiment in 1919. He traveled to an eclipse that was a particularly favorable eclipse when the Sun's position among the stars was projected among a large number of very bright stars. He was able to measure the displacement of the stars from their true positions. The stars are circled here. That's their measured positions, there in the middle of these circles, and he measured them to be displaced from their true position. (You actually can't see the stars in this photograph.)

You might ask, "How do you know the true positions?" Wait six months, when the sky is not lit up by the Sun in that part of the sky. Wait six months, when the Earth is on the opposite side of the Sun and take a picture of that part of the sky in the dark night. You will see the true positions of those stars. A similar photograph during a total eclipse shows the apparent positions when the Sun is in the way. It's the difference between the true and apparent positions that is the shift that Einstein predicted.

The shift was confirmed, and Einstein became an overnight celebrity because of this experiment. Here is a postcard that Einstein wrote to his mother, saying that he had just received communication from a colleague that Eddington had measured the predicted effect. This was the first independent test of the general theory of relativity. There had been some predictions already, but the difference was that those effects were known before Einstein developed relativity so one could say that he developed relativity to explain those effects. It's good to be able to do that, but the true test in any scientific theory is to predict a phenomenon that has not yet been observed, to go out and measure it, and see whether the prediction is confirmed. This was the first such prediction of relativity that was confirmed. It made Einstein an overnight celebrity, and from that point on he became possibly the most famous scientist ever to have lived, with the exception of Newton and perhaps a few others like Galileo.

Now let's very briefly consider the related phenomenon of eclipses of the Moon. Eclipses of the Moon occur when the Moon passes through Earth's shadow. Earth's shadow is much bigger than the Moon's shadow, so it takes awhile for the Moon to actually pass through the shadow of the Earth. A lunar eclipse therefore lasts quite some time. Totality lasts for about an hour and the partial phases last for another half hour or so, on either side.

Here is a partially eclipsed Moon. You can see that part of the Moon has entered Earth's shadow, but part is still illuminated by the Sun. The fully eclipsed Moon appears kind of red and not uniformly dark everywhere. What is the cause of that? If you look at this diagram here, you can see the geometry during a total lunar eclipse. Sunlight is entering from the left. It consists of white light, a mixture of all the different colors—reds, greens and blues. The Earth blocks almost all of them when they hit the Earth, but the Earth is not a solid sphere with a vacuum surrounding it. The Earth has a thin atmosphere, and the Sun's rays pass through that atmosphere and are refracted or bent toward the Moon, just as a prism bends light when light passes through it. Some sunlight actually gets bent toward the Moon and illuminates the Moon during totality.

That's why the Moon is not entirely dark during totality. It's red because of the same effect that causes red sunsets, red moonrises and red moonsets. The part of the sunlight that is passing through the atmosphere towards the Moon is scattered and absorbed, especially the blue wavelengths. The blues, greens and violets are scattered and absorbed much more than the orange and red light, simply because of the properties of dust in the atmosphere and the molecules in the atmosphere.

So, the reds and oranges survive whereas the greens, blues and violets do not. What you have then is a totally eclipsed Moon, which has different shades of orange or red, or whatever, depending on how much of the sunlight passed through the atmosphere and managed to reach the Moon.

The shades of orange and red and the degree of illumination of the Moon depend on a number of factors. Here in this stunning photograph, you can see the projection of the Earth's shadow at the position of the Moon. This is a multiple exposure as the Moon was being eclipsed by the Earth's shadow. You can see that the Earth's shadow is pretty big compared with the Moon. The Moon might pass, depending on the geometry, through the central region of the shadow, in which case it would be quite dark because most of the light that is actually able to be bent toward the Moon is bent more toward the outer edges of Earth's shadow because the bending effect is not extremely large. The Moon would appear dark, if it was going through the middle of the shadow, and it would appear somewhat brighter if it were going through the edge of the shadow. In particular, the edge of the Moon, which is right near the edge of the shadow, would see quite a lot of sunlight bent by the Earth's atmosphere.

Quite often during a lunar eclipse, you will have part of the Moon appear quite bright, as in this picture; the upper right part of the Moon looks brighter than the lower left part of the Moon. That's because it's closer to the edge of the Earth's shadow, so more of the Sun's light can reach the Moon. Less of the Sun's light can be bent all the way down toward the part of the Moon that's more in the depths of Earth's shadow, so that part looks darker.

Moreover, the degree of darkening and the degree of orange and red colors depends on how much dust and other debris there is in the atmosphere. We know that on a smoggy day or during times of wild fires, the Sun and the Moon appear considerably redder than when the atmosphere is clear. Again, that's because there's more dust particles there absorbing the blues, the greens and the violets. When you have a nice clear day without smog and forest fire smoke, you tend to see the greens and the blues mixed in with the oranges and reds and that gives you a more white color.

If the atmosphere has a lot of debris in it during the time of an eclipse, you will see a more reddened Moon, a darker Moon. Eclipses that have occurred shortly after the time of large volcanic eruptions have tended to be a deeper red than eclipses that have occurred away from the times of giant volcanic eruptions. Eclipses that are seen in regions of wild fires or debris or smoke from factories and things like that tend to be redder as well because that part of the Moon that's visible is being illuminated by light that's passing through a dusty atmosphere.

One final thing to note is that, clearly, the geometry of a lunar eclipse is such that everyone on the dark side of the Earth—everyone who can see the full moon, which is essentially everyone with a clear horizon on the dark side of the Earth—will see the fully eclipsed Moon. The geometry is such that the Sun, say, is over there, here's the Earth, and here's the Moon. Everyone who can see the full moon will see an eclipsed Moon. So, you don't have to be at a particular location on Earth's surface to see the eclipsed Moon. You will see it everywhere where you can see a full moon. That will be the case for everyone who can see the Moon. Lunar eclipses don't require the extensive travel to far corners of the globe that solar eclipses do. They're well worth seeing, so go out and enjoy the glorious eclipses.

Useful symbols

In these course notes, the following mathematical symbols are used. "~" means "roughly" or "around"; "≈" means "approximately equal to" (basically synonymous with "~"); "≥" means "greater than or equal to"; "≤" means "less than or equal to"; ">>" means "much greater than; "<<" means "much less than"; "∝" means "proportional to."

Glossary

absorption line: A wavelength (or small range of wavelengths) at which the brightness of a spectrum is lower than it is at neighboring wavelengths.

accretion: The transfer of matter to the surface of a star or a black hole. When the transferred matter goes into orbit around the object, an "accretion disk" is formed.

active galaxy: A galaxy whose nucleus emits large quantities of electromagnetic radiation that does not appear to be produced by stars.

Ångstrom (Å): A unit of length commonly used for visible wavelengths of light; 1 Å = 10^{-8} cm.

angular momentum: A measure of the amount of spin of an object; dependent on the object's rotation rate, mass, and mass distribution.

antiparticle: A particle whose charge (if not neutral) and certain other properties are opposite those of a corresponding particle of the same mass. An encounter between a particle and its antiparticle results in mutual annihilation and the production of high-energy photons.

apparent brightness: The amount of energy received from an object per second, per square cm of collecting area. It is related to luminosity and distance through the equation $b = L/(4\pi d^2)$.

asteroid: chunk of rock, smaller than a planet, that generally orbits the Sun between Mars and Jupiter.

Astronomical unit (A.U.): The average distance between the Sun and the Earth (1.5×10^8 km).

aurora: The northern or southern lights, caused by energetic particles interacting with atoms and ions in Earth's upper atmosphere, making them glow.

Big Bang: The birth of the Universe in a very hot, dense state about 14 billion years ago, followed by the expansion of space.

binary pulsar: A pulsar in a binary system. Often this term is used for systems in which the pulsar's companion is another neutron star.

binary star: Two stars gravitationally bound to (and orbiting) each other

black body: An object that absorbs all radiation that hits it; none is transmitted or reflected. It emits a spectrum whose shape depends only on the temperature of the object.

black hole: A region of spacetime in which the gravitational field is so strong that nothing, not even light, can escape. Predicted by Einstein's general theory of relativity.

brown dwarf: A gravitationally bound object that is insufficiently massive to be a star, but too massive for a planet. Generally the mass range is taken to be 10–80 Jupiter masses.

CCD: Charge-coupled device. A solid-state imaging chip whose properties include high sensitivity, large dynamic range, and linearity.

celestial sphere: The enormous sphere, centered on the Earth, to which the stars appear to be fixed.

centrifugal force: The outward force felt by an object in a rotating frame of reference.

Cepheid: A type of pulsating star that varies in brightness with a period of 1 to 100 days. Cepheids with long periods are more luminous than those with short periods.

Chandrasekhar limit: The maximum stable mass of a white dwarf or the iron core of a massive star, above which degeneracy pressure is unable to provide sufficient support; about 1.4 solar masses.

comet: An interplanetary chunk of ice and rock, often in a very elongated orbit, that produces a diffuse patch of light in the sky when relatively near the Sun due to evaporation of the ice.

constellation: One of 88 regions into which the celestial sphere is divided. The pattern of bright stars within a constellation is often named in honor of a god, person, or animal.

core: In a main-sequence star, roughly the central 10 percent by mass. In an evolved star, usually refers to the degenerate central region.

corona: The very hot, tenuous, outermost region of the Sun, seen during a total solar eclipse.

cosmic background radiation: Microwave (radio) electromagnetic radiation that was produced in the hot Big Bang. It now corresponds to $T \approx 3$ K due to the expansion and cooling of the Universe.

cosmic rays: High-energy protons and other charged particles, probably formed by supernovae and other violent processes.

cosmological constant: In Einstein's general theory of relativity, a term (Λ) that produces an acceleration of the Universe's expansion.

cosmological principle: The Universe is homogeneous and isotropic on the largest scales.

cosmology: The study of the overall structure and evolution of the Universe.

critical density: The average density of the Universe if it were poised exactly between eternal expansion and ultimate collapse.

dark matter: Invisible matter that dominates the mass of the Universe.

degenerate gas: A peculiar state of matter at high densities in which, according to the laws of quantum physics, the particles move very rapidly in well-defined energy levels and exert tremendous pressure.

dipole field: The pattern of electric field lines produced by a pair of equal and opposite electric charges, or of a magnetic field lines surrounding a bar magnet.

Doppler shift: The change in wavelength or frequency produced when a source of waves and the observer more relative to each other. Blueshifts (to shorter wavelengths) and redshifts (to longer wavelengths) are associated with approach and recession, respectively.

$E = mc^2$: Einstein's famous formula for the equivalence of mass and energy.

eclipse: The passage of one celestial body into the shadow of another, or the obscuration of one celestial body by another body passing in front of it.

electromagnetic force: One of the four fundamental forces of nature; it holds electrons in atoms, etc.

electromagnetic radiation: Self-propagating, oscillating, electric and magnetic fields. From shortest to longest wavelengths: gamma rays, X-rays, ultraviolet, optical (visible), infrared, and radio.

electron: Low-mass, negatively charged, fundamental particle that normally "orbits" an atomic nucleus.

electroweak force: The unification of the electromagnetic and weak nuclear forces.

ellipse: A set of points (curve) such that the sum of the distances to two given points (foci) is constant.

emission line: A wavelength (or small range of wavelengths) at which the brightness of a spectrum is higher than it is at neighboring wavelengths.

erg: A unit of energy (work) in the metric system, equal to a force of one dyne ($g-cm/s^2$) acting through a distance of one cm.

escape velocity: The minimum speed an object must have to escape the gravitational pull of another object.

event horizon: The boundary of a black hole from within which nothing can escape.

galaxy: A large (typically 5000 to 200,000 light years in diameter), gravitationally bound system of hundreds of millions (and up to a trillion) stars. Galaxy shapes are generally spiral or elliptical, and sometimes irregular or peculiar.

general theory of relativity: Einstein's comprehensive theory of mass (energy), space, and time; it states that mass produces a curvature of spacetime which we associate with the force of gravity.

grand unified theory (GUT): A theory in which unifies the strong nuclear ("color") and electroweak forces into a single interaction. It is not known which, if any, of the proposed GUTs is correct.

gravity: The weakest of nature's fundamental forces, but the dominant force over large distances because it is cumulative; all matter and energy contributes, regardless of charge.

great circle: The intersection of a sphere with a plane passing through the center of the sphere.

Hertzsprung-Russell (H-R) diagram: A plot of the surface temperature (or color) versus luminosity (power, or absolute brightness) for a group of stars.

homogeneous: The same (density, temperature, etc.) at all locations.

horizon: The great circle on the celestial sphere that is 90° away from the zenith

Hubble's law: The linear relation between the distance and recession speed of a distant object: $v = H_0 d$. The constant of proportionality, H_0, is called Hubble's constant.

inflationary universe: A modification of the standard Big Bang theory. Very early in its history (e.g., $t \approx 10^{-36}$ seconds), when the Universe was exceedingly small, it began a period of rapidly accelerating expansion, making its final size truly enormous. Subsequently, the regular Big Bang expansion ensued.

interferometer: Two or more telescopes used together to produce high resolution images.

interstellar medium: The space between the stars, filled to some extent with gas and dust.

ionized: Having lost at least one electron. Atoms become ionized primarily by the absorption of energetic photons and by collisions with other particles.

isotopes: Atomic nuclei having the same number of protons but different numbers of neutrons.

isotropic: The same in all directions (i.e., no preferred alignment).

Kelvin: The size of 1 degree on the Kelvin ("absolute") temperature scale, in which absolute zero is 0 K, water freezes at 273 K, and water boils at 373 K. To convert from the Kelvin scale to the Celsius (centigrade; C) scale, subtract 273 from the Kelvin scale value. Degrees Fahrenheit (F) = (9/5)C + 32.

Kepler's third law: If one object orbits another, the square of its period of revolution is proportional to the cube of the major (long) axis of the elliptical orbit.

Large Magellanic Cloud: A dwarf companion galaxy of our Milky Way Galaxy about 170,000 light years away; best seen from Earth's Southern Hemisphere.

light curve: A plot of an object's brightness as a function of time.

light year: The distance light travels through a vacuum in 1 year; about 10 trillion km.

luminosity: Power; the total energy emitted by an object per unit time.

magnitude: A logarithmic measure of apparent brightness; a difference of 5 magnitudes corresponds to a brightness ratio of 100. Typical very bright stars have mag 1; the faintest naked-eye stars have mag 6.

main sequence: The phase of stellar evolution, lasting about 90 percent of a star's life, during which the star fuses hydrogen to helium in its core.

meteor: The streak of light in the sky produced when an interplanetary rock enters Earth's atmosphere and burns up due to friction. If the rock reaches Earth's surface, it is called a meteorite.

meteoroid: An interplanetary rock that is not in the asteroid belt.

nebula: A region containing an above-average density of interstellar gas and dust.

neutrino: A nearly massless, uncharged, fundamental particle that interacts exceedingly weakly with matter. There are three types: electron, muon, and tau neutrinos.

neutron: Massive, uncharged particle that is normally part of an atomic nucleus.

neutron star: The compact endpoint in stellar evolution in which typically 1.4 solar masses of material is compressed into a small (diameter = 20–30 km) sphere supported by neutron degeneracy pressure.

nova: A star that suddenly brightens by a factor of 10^2 to 10^6, due to energetic processes (sudden accretion of matter, or nuclear fusion) at the surface of a white dwarf or (less frequently) a neutron star.

nuclear fusion: Reactions in which low-mass atomic nuclei combine to form a more massive nucleus.

nucleosynthesis: The creation of elements through nuclear reactions, generally nuclear fusion.

Olbers's paradox: The dark night sky; simple arguments suggest that it should be very bright.

parsec: A unit of distance equal to 3.26 light years (3.086×10^{13} km).

phase transition: The transformation of matter from one phase (e.g., liquid) to another (e.g., solid).

photon: A quantum, or package, of electromagnetic radiation that travels at the speed of light. From highest to lowest energies: gamma rays, X-rays, ultraviolet, optical (visible), infrared, and radio.

photosphere: The visible surface of the Sun (or another star) from which light escapes into space.

planet: An object of substantial size (diameter > 1000 km) that orbits a star, but not massive enough for nuclear fusion ever to begin. An upper limit of about 0.01 solar masses is generally adopted.

planetary nebula: A shell of gas, expelled by a red giant star near the end of its life (but before the white dwarf stage), which glows because it is ionized by ultraviolet radiation from the star's remaining core.

planetary system: A collection of planets and smaller bodies orbiting a star (e.g., our Solar System).

planetesimals: Small bodies, such as meteoroids and comets, into which the solar nebula condensed and from which the planets subsequently formed.

positron: The antiparticle of an electron.

progenitor: In the case of a supernova, the star that will eventually explode.

proteins: Molecules consisting of long chains of amino acids.

proton: Massive, positively charged particle that is normal part of an atomic nucleus. The number of protons in the nucleus determines the chemical element.

protostar: A star still in the process of forming, embedded in a thick collapsing envelope of gas and dust.

pulsar: An astronomical object detected through pulses of radiation (usually radio waves) having a short, extremely well-defined period; thought to be a rotating neutron star with a very strong magnetic field.

quantum fluctuations: The spontaneous (but short-lived) quantum creation of particles out of nothing.

quantum mechanics: A 20th century theory that successfully describes the behavior of matter on very small scales (such as atoms) and radiation.

quark: A fundamental particle with fractional charge, and of which protons and neutrons consist.

quasar: A star-like, extremely luminous object, typically billions of light years away. Now thought to be the nucleus of a galaxy with a supermassive black hole that is accreting matter from its vicinity.

radial velocity: The speed of an object along the line of sight to the observer.

red giant: The evolutionary phase following the main sequence of a relatively low-mass star like the Sun; the star grows in size and luminosity, but has a cooler surface.

redshift: Defined to be $z = (\lambda - \lambda_0)/\lambda_0$, where λ_0 is the rest wavelength of a given spectral line and λ is its (longer) observed wavelength. The wavelength shift may be caused by recession of the source from the observer, or to the propagation of light out of a gravitational field.

resolution: The clarity of detail produced by a given optical system (telescope, etc.).

rest mass: The mass of an object that is at rest with respect to the observer. The effective mass increases with speed. Only massless particles can (and indeed, must) travel at the speed of light.

retrograde motion: The apparent "backwards" (east to west) motion among the stars that planets undergo for a short time each year.

Schwarzschild radius: The radius to which a given mass must be compressed to form a nonrotating black hole. Also, the radius of the event horizon of a nonrotating black hole.

singularity: A mathematical point of zero volume associated with infinite values for physical parameters such as density.

solar mass: The mass of the Sun, 1.99×10^{33} grams, about 330,000 times the mass of the Earth.

spacetime: The four-dimensional fabric of the Universe whose points are events having specific locations in space (three dimensions) and time (one dimension).

spectrum: A plot of the brightness of electromagnetic radiation from an object as a function of wavelength or frequency.

star cluster: A gravitationally bound group of stars that formed from the same nebula.

Steady-state universe: A model of the expanding Universe based on the assumption that the properties of the Universe do not change with time. Matter must be continually created to maintain constant density.

strong nuclear force: The strongest force, it binds protons and neutrons together in a nucleus. Actually, it is the residue of the even stronger "color force" that binds quarks together in a proton or neutron.

supergiant: The evolutionary phase following the main sequence of a massive star; the star becomes more luminous and larger. If its size increases by a very large factor, it becomes cool (red).

supernova: The violent explosion of a star at the end of its life. Hydrogen is present or absent in the spectra of Type II or Type I supernovae, respectively.

supernova remnant: The cloud of chemically enriched gases ejected into space by a supernova.

tidal force: The difference between the gravitational force exerted by one body on the near and far sides of another body.

time dilation: According to relativity theory, the slowing of time perceived by an observer watching another object moving rapidly or located in a strong gravitational field.

transverse velocity: The speed of an object across the plane of the sky (perpendicular to the line of sight).

Universe: All that there is within the space and time dimensions accessible to us, as well as regions beyond (but still physically connected to) those that we can see.

variable star: A star whose apparent brightness changes with time.

weak nuclear force: Governs the decay of a neutron into a proton, electron, and antineutrino.

white dwarf: The evolutionary end point of stars that have initial mass less than about 8 solar masses. All that remains is the electron-degenerate core of helium or carbon-oxygen (in some cases O–Ne–Mg).

wormhole: The connection between two black holes in separate universes, or in different parts of our Universe. Also called an Einstein-Rosen bridge.

zenith: The point on the celestial sphere that is directly above the observer.

Universe Timeline

(For $t > 10^{14}$ years, assume Universe expands forever.)

"0" seconds: The birth of the Universe, perhaps from a quantum fluctuation.

10^{-43} seconds: Space-time foam? Gravity and grand unified force become separate.

10^{-37} seconds? Inflation begins.

10^{-35} seconds? Inflation ends. Strong nuclear and electroweak forces become separate.

10^{-11} seconds: Weak nuclear and electromagnetic forces become separate.

10^{-6} seconds: Matter/antimatter annihilation; slight excess of protons and neutrons.

1 second: Electrons and positrons annihilate; slight excess of electrons.

10^2 seconds: Nucleosynthesis of lightest elements from protons and neutrons.

3×10^5 years (10^{13} seconds): Formation of neutral atoms; Universe transparent.

3×10^6 years (10^{14} seconds)? First stars begin to form, but not in galaxies.

10^9 years (3×10^{16} seconds): Many galaxies form and begin assembling into clusters.

10^{10} years: Solar System forms (4.6 billion years ago).

1.4×10^{10} years: Present age of the Universe.

2×10^{10} years: Sun becomes a red giant and subsequently a white dwarf.

10^{14} years: Last low-mass stars die.

10^{20} years: Most stars and planets gravitationally ejected from galaxies.

10^{30} years: Black holes swallow most of the remaining objects in galaxies.

10^{38} years? All objects except black holes disintegrate, due to proton decay.

10^{65} years: Stellar-mass black holes evaporate due to Hawking process.

10^{100} years: Largest galaxy-mass black holes evaporate.

10^{110} years? Positronium atoms (electron-positron pairs) decay, producing photons.

Solar System Timeline

(Given in terms of years ago; 0 = today)

4.6 billion years: Solar System forms.

3.9 billion years: Heavy bombardment of Earth by planetesimals subsides.

3.8 billion years: Possible formation of primitive life (definitely by 3.5 billion years).

2 billion years: Free oxygen begins to accumulate in atmosphere, due to photosynthesis.

600 million years: Present atmosphere essentially complete. Multicellular life flourishes.

550 million years: "Cambrian explosion"—formation of complex, hard-bodied animals.

240 million years: Mesozoic Era—earliest dinosaurs appear.

65 million years: Extinction of the dinosaurs, along with 2/3 of all living species.

3.5 million years: The first *hominids* appear.

350 thousand years: Early *homo sapiens* appear.

3 thousand years: Beginning of Iron Age.

250 years: Industrial Revolution.

100 years: Radio communication.

Biographical Notes

Aristarchus of Samos ($\sim$ 310 – $\sim$ 230 B.C.). Greek astronomer; measured the Sun–Earth distance relative to the Earth–Moon distance. Realized that the Sun is much larger than the Earth, and reasoned that the Sun (rather than the Earth) is at the center of the Universe, predating Copernicus by 1800 years.

Aristotle (384–322 B.C.). The most influential early Greek philosopher; he lectured on a vast range of subjects. Most of his beliefs in physics and astronomy were wrong. Developed a widely adopted geocentric (Earth-centered) model of the Universe consisting of 55 spheres. Correctly concluded the Earth is spherical.

Brahe, Tycho (1546–1601). Danish astronomer; measured the positions of planets with unprecedented accuracy, laying the foundations for Kepler's work. Discovered and studied a bright supernova in 1572; thus, the "sphere of fixed stars" is not immutable, in contradiction to Aristotelian and Christian dogma.

Copernicus, Nicolaus (1473–1543). Polish astronomer; proposed the heliocentric (Sun-centered) model of the planetary system. He showed how the retrograde motion of planets could be explained with this hypothesis. His book, *De Revolutionibus*, was published the year of his death.

Einstein, Albert (1879–1955). German-American physicist, the most important since Newton. Developed the special and general theories of relativity, proposed that light consists of photons, and worked out the theory of Brownian motion (irregular zigzag motion of particles suspended in a fluid, due to collisions with molecules). Responsible for $e = mc^2$, perhaps the most famous equation in the world.

Galileo Galilei (1564–1542). Italian mathematician, astronomer, and physicist; was the first to systematically study the heavens with a telescope. Discovered the phases of Venus and the four bright moons of Jupiter, providing strong evidence against the geocentric model for the Solar System. After being sentenced by the Inquisition to perpetual house arrest, he studied the motions of falling bodies, laying the experimental groundwork for Newton's laws of motion.

Gamow, George (1904–1968). Russian-American physicist; he suggested that the Universe began in a hot, compressed state and predicted the existence of the cosmic background radiation that was later discovered by Arno Penzias and Robert Wilson. Also devised a theory of radioactive decay.

Guth, Alan (1947–). American physicist; proposed the inflationary theory of the Universe to eliminate some glaring problems with the standard Big Bang model. His perspective was that of an elementary particle physicist, not an astronomer; he was most troubled by the absence of magnetic monopoles.

Hawking, Stephen (1942–). English physicist, best known for his remarkable theoretical work while physically incapacitated by Lou Gehrig's disease (AMS). His prediction that black holes can evaporate through quantum tunneling is an important step in attempts to unify quantum physics and gravity (general relativity). He is Lucasian Professor of Mathematics at Cambridge University, as was Newton.

Hoyle, Fred (1915–). English astronomer; proposed the "steady-state theory" of the Universe, which stimulated much important work in cosmology. Also made fundamental contributions to the understanding of the origin of the chemical elements. Coined the term "Big Bang."

Hubble, Edwin (1889–1953). American astronomer, after whom the Hubble Space Telescope is named. He proved that "spiral nebulae" are galaxies far outside our own Milky Way, and discovered the expansion of the Universe ("Hubble's law") by recognizing that the redshift of a galaxy is proportional to its distance. He also proposed a widely used morphological classification scheme for galaxies.

Kepler, Johannes (1571–1630). German mathematician and astronomer; was Tycho's assistant, and gained access to his data after his death. Developed three empirical laws of planetary motion that represent a significant revision of the Copernican model. Studied a very bright supernova in 1604.

Leavitt, Henrietta (1868–1921). American astronomer; demonstrated a relationship between the period and luminosity of Cepheid variable stars. This was done by analysis of Cepheids clustered together and therefore at the same distance, so that differences in brightness indicated luminosity differences.

Maxwell, James (1831–1879). Scottish physicist; showed that visible light is only one form of electromagnetic radiation, whose speed can be derived from a set of four equations that describe all of electricity and magnetism. Also investigated heat and the kinetic theory of gases.

Newton, Isaac (1642–1727). English mathematician and physicist; developed three laws of motion and the law of universal gravitation, all published in *The Principia*. Invented the reflecting telescope, determined that white light consists of all colors of the rainbow, and invented calculus. At age 27, became Lucasian Professor of Mathematics, Cambridge University. Became Warden of the Mint in 1696; knighted in 1705.

Ptolemy, Claudius (~ 100 – ~ 170). Greek astronomer who developed an elaborate model for planetary motions, based on Aristotle's geocentric universe, that endured for over 1400 years. Compiled the *Almagest*, a set of 13 volumes that provides most of our knowledge of early Greek astronomy.

Rubin, Vera (1928–). American astronomer; was the first to observationally show that the rotation curves of spiral galaxies imply the presence of considerable "dark matter." She also obtained early evidence for large-scale "peculiar motions" of galaxies relative to the smooth expansion of the Universe.

Sagan, Carl (1934–1996). American astronomer, and the 20th century's most well known popularizer of science, especially astronomy. Among his scientific accomplishments, he demonstrated that Venus suffers from an enormous greenhouse effect. *Cosmos*, his 13-episode public-television astronomy series, has been seen by about 500 million people. He was an eloquent proponent of unmanned Solar System exploration.

Sandage, Allan (1926–). American astronomer and disciple of Edwin Hubble, he has made fundamental contributions to the determination of globular cluster ages, the distances of galaxies, the Hubble constant, the age of the Universe, and the rate at which the expansion of the Universe is changing.

Shapley, Harlow (1885–1972). American astronomer; correctly deduced that the Sun is not at the center of the Milky Way Galaxy, and that the Galaxy is larger than previously believed. Incorrectly concluded that the "spiral nebulae" are within the Milky Way, but most of his reasoning was logically sound.

Zwicky, Fritz (1898–1974). Swiss-American astronomer; proposed that supernovae result from the collapse of the cores of massive stars, producing neutron stars and energetic particles (cosmic rays).

Compiled an extensive atlas of galaxy clusters, and showed that many such clusters must contain dark matter in order to be gravitationally bound.

Credits

The Jewel Box NGC 4755(Anglo-Australian Observatory, Photograph By David Malin #25.)

Gravitational Lens CL0024+1654. (NASA, Hubble Space Telescope 20-10, #16)

Planetary nebula NGC 6543 (NASA, Hubble Space Telescope 20-6, #7)

Black Hole in M87 Core (NASA, Hubble Space Telescope 20-5, #6)

Mirror at Perkin-Elmer (NASA, Hubble Space Telescope /STScI)

Star Cluster R136 Ground Based Image, 2.2 m telescope. (Georges Meylan and European Southern Observatory)

Star Cluster R136 Processed Image (NASA, Hubble Space Telescope /STScI)

Astronaut Jeff Hoffman & WFPC1 during EVA#3 (NASA, Hubble Space Telescope 20-3, #4)

Comparison Image M100 Galactic Nucleus (NASA, Hubble Space Telescope 20-3, #13)

Launch of STS-31 (NASA, Hubble Space Telescope /STScI)

Spherical Aberration Shown in Star Seen with Hubble Space Telescope PC (NASA, Hubble Space Telescope /STScI)

M16 Gaseous Pillars, (NASA, Hubble Space Telescope 20-7, #9)

Hourglass Nebula - Planetary Nebula(NASA, Hubble Space Telescope 20-10, #13)

Atmospheric Effects, (NASA, Hubble Space Telescope 20-4, #11)

Four Faces of Mars, (NASA, Hubble Space Telescope 20-14, #3)

Couch and Ellis; Abell 2218 gravitational lens (NASA, Hubble Space Telescope 4/5/95)

Hubble Deep Field WFPC2 chip (NASA, Hubble Space Telescope 20-10, #6)

Peculiar Galaxies (NASA, Hubble Space Telescope 20-5, #19)

Saturn (NASA, Hubble Space Telescope /STScI 90-11, WFPC 8/90)

Protoplanetary Disks in Orion Nebula (NASA, Hubble Space Telescope 20-10, #1)

Owens Valley Radio Observatory - single dish. (Alex Filippenko)

Keck segments and Luis Ho., Oct. 1994 (Alex Filippenko)

CCD in hand, Oct. 15, 1991(Alex Filippenko)

Spectrum - rainbow colors(Alex Filippenko)

Meteor near north celestial pole, Sept. 1978 (Alex Filippenko)

San Jose, from Lick Observatory, Sept. 1977 (Alex Filippenko)

Star trails in Sagittarius (Alex Filippenko)

Partial eclipse crescents, 07/11/91 (Alex Filippenko)

Peru eclipse glasses, Nov. 1994 (Alex Filippenko)

Projection of Sun with telescope, 07/11/91 (Alex Filippenko)

"Heaven Photographed by Hubble Telescope." Weekly World News, April 30, 1996

Lick 3-m Shane telescope (University Of California /Lick Observatory)

Orion nebula, central region (University Of California /Lick Observatory)

Lick 36-inch refractor (University Of California /Lick Observatory)

Lick 3-m Shane mirror, with people looking (University Of California /Lick Observatory)

Nicolas Copernicus (Library of Congress)

Albert Einstein writing on blackboard, Astronomical Society Of The Pacific #15 Past Astronomers, (Cargenie Observatories)

Arthur Eddington, Astronomical Society Of The Pacific #14 Past Astronomers(Courtesy Astronomical Society Of The Pacific)

Moon, age 4 days, #L1 (University Of California /Lick Observatory)

Moon, age 7 days (first quarter), #L2 (University Of California /Lick Observatory)

Moon, age 10 days, #L3 (University Of California /Lick Observatory)

Moon, age 14 days (full moon), #L4 (University Of California /Lick Observatory)

Moon, age 20 days, #L5 (University Of California /Lick Observatory)

Earthrise over Moon (Jet Propulsion Labs-4, #16)

Moon, age 22 days, #L6 (University Of California /Lick Observatory)

Moon, age 24 days, #L7 (University Of California /Lick Observatory)

Earth (Jet Propulsion Lab-4, #6)

Summary of Planets Discovered (8 systems)(Astronomical Society Of The Pacific #25)

Search for Planets (Geoff Marcy & Paul Butler)

Here lies the body of James Lick (Alex Filippenko)

Rays of light to Earth, from Sun at different distances; #34 (Saunders College Publishing)

Explanation of the seasons; #13 (Saunders College Publishing)

Light rays through Schmidt telescope; bottom of #30(Saunders College Publishing)

Electromagnetic spectrum, and visible light (red to violet); #40 (Saunders College Publishing)

Planck curves for different temperatures; #43(Saunders College Publishing)

Spectra: continuous, absorption, emission in different directions; #46(Saunders College Publishing)

Cause of Moon's phases — times indicated, face-on view; #54 (Saunders College Publishing)

Hydrogen atom energy levels — equally spaced circles; #51(Saunders College Publishing)

Armstrong's Foot on Lunar Surface (Jet Propulsion Labs 40-55, #12)

Spectra of 4 different emission-line gases; #45 (Saunders college Publishing)

Schematic of proton-proton chain; #134 (Saunders College Publishing)

Sunspot cycle, no Maunder minimum; #131 (Saunders College Publishing)

Light rays through lens; top of #29 (Saunders College Publishing)

Sunspots and solar granules; #5010 (National Optical Astronomy Observatories)

Sunset, annular eclipse; #5018 (National Optical Astronomy Observatories)

Globular cluster M15; #1103 (National Optical Astronomy Observatories)

3C 273 and optical jet; #2500 (National Optical Astronomy Observatories)

Mosaic of 4 CCDs; #7103 (National Optical Astronomy Observatories)

Solar flare, white light; #4158 (National Optical Astronomy Observatories)

Crab nebula, optical; 03//27/97 (Dr. Sharp, National Optical Astronomy Observatories)

Aldrin deploys Passive EASEP's Seismic Experiment (Jet Propulsion Labs 40-55, #22)

16 Cygni A+B double star; 04/22/97. (Dr. Sharp, National Optical Astronomy Observatories)

Moon Rock on Display in Houston (Jet Propulsion Labs 40-55, #39)

Temperature Variations in CBR. (NASA and Astronomical Society Of The Pacific #16 COBE)

Human and Match in IR. (NASA and Astronomical Society Of The Pacific #02 IRAS Gallery)

Trifid nebula (Hale Observatories, California Institute of Technology)

NGC 1976 M-42, Orion nebula, 200-inch; S-23 (Hale Observatories, California Institute of Technology)

Black hole — curved spacetime on LMC ("Mercury" cover, Astronomical Society Of The Pacific)

Crab nebula pulsar (NASA and Astronomical Society Of The Pacific #14 ROSAT)

Venus taken from Mariner 10. XA-19 #1 Venus (NASA)

Prominence and diamond ring #7 Glorious eclipses (Dennis di Cicco)

Fully eclipsed moon, close-up #19 Glorious eclipses (Dennis di Cicco)

Partially eclipsed moon #17 Glorious eclipses (Dennis di Cicco)

Chromosphere through red filter #15 Glorious eclipses (Dennis di Cicco)

Baily's beads and chromosphere #14 Glorious eclipses (Dennis di Cicco)

Annular eclipse sequence #12 Glorious eclipses (Dennis di Cicco)

Four early quasars (Hale Observatories, California Institute of Technology)

Radio Interferometer; #183 (Saunders College Publishing)

Arecibo Observatory, Puerto Rico (Cornell University and Science Photo Library; photograph by David Parker, 1997)

1966 Leonid Storm meteors, Tri-X film (Scott Murrell)

Phases of Venus, compared with Jupiter(Owen Gingerich)

Haircut by camel barber, 1995 India eclipse (Owen Gingerich)

Earth and Moon #6 Galileo (NASA)

Meteorite with Fusion Crust #10 Ancient Life on Mars (NASA)

Aristotle's model (Owen Gingerich and the Houghton Library, Harvard University)

Different distances of stars in Big Dipper (Saunders College Publishing)

Affect of aperture size on resolution (Saunders College Publishing)

Inclined light - less heating(Saunders College Publishing)

Four supernovae (Adam Riess)

Path of Sun in different seasons (Saunders College Publishing)

Self-reproducing universes (Andrei Linde)

Zenith and horizon as viewed by person (Saunders College Publishing)

Position of Sun at different seasons (Saunders College Publishing)

The Big Dipper: shape vs. time (Saunders College Publishing)

Formation of continuous spectrum: prism (Saunders College Publishing)

Einstein: letter to mother after eclipse (Owen Gingerich)

James Lick: photo, Univ. of California, Santa Cruz (Shane Archive)

Isaac Newton: photo, Univ. of California, Santa Cruz (Shane Archive)

Rotation of Sun: sunspots (Hale Observatories)

Sun: exceptionally large sunspot, 1947 April 7 (Hale Observatories, California Institute of Technology)

The Sun: full disk (National Optical Astronomy Observatories)

Solar prominence: detail (National Optical Astronomy Observatories)

Size of Earth's shadow at moon "Glorious eclipses" #16 (Akira Fujii)

Sequence of solar eclipse over Mexican church. "Glorious eclipses" #2 (Akira Fujii)

1991 solar eclipse: totality "Glorious eclipses" #1 (Sky Publishing Corporation)

Sun: partial eclipse "Glorious eclipses" #6 (Sky Publishing Corporation)

Sun: diamond ring "Glorious eclipses" #9 (James Curry)

Andromeda galaxy #8 (Bill and Sally Fletcher)

Crescent moon, Earthshine; San Francisco (Niranjan Thatte)

Very Large Array, NM Radio Universe #3 (National Radio Astronomy Observatory/American Universities Incorporated)

Brilliant G impact, Comet SL-9/Jupiter (Peter McGregor; Australian National University)

1922 Australia eclipse, stars marked, Univ. of California, Santa Cruz (Shane archive)

BIMA array, many dishes (University of California, Berkeley)

IRAS satellite, drawing (NASA and Jet Propulsion Labs-6-18)

Lick 3-m telescope with laser (Claire Max, LLNL)

Black hole, prize-winning photo (Alex Filippenko)

Galileo's telescopes - best (Museum of Science, Florence, Italy)

1991 eclipse map - partial phases (Sky Publishing Corporation)

Headline, "Signs of Life on Mars" (San Jose Mercury News)

Keck adaptive optics simulation (California Association for Research in Astronomy)

Big Dipper and Ursa Major (Science Graphics)

Highest Resolution Image of Gaspra (Jet Propulsion Labs)

Inner solar system (NASA)

Two Keck domes (Richard Wainscoat)

Summit of Mauna Kea (Richard Wainscoat)

Keck primary mirror, with person in center. (California Association for Research in Astronomy)

Total solar eclipse, 1991 Prominences, chromosphere, inner corona(James Curry)

Corona overhead at India 1995 eclipse (Jay Pasachoff)

Conic sections, and Kepler's second law (Saunders College Publishing)

Celestial sphere: definitions (Saunders College Publishing)

Schematic of H and He atoms (Saunders College Publishing)

Rotation of celestial sphere (Saunders College Publishing)

Parabola focusing light rays (Saunders College Publishing)

3 types of reflector telescopes (Saunders College Publishing)

Size of Sun, Earth, white dwarf (Saunders College Publishing)

Water waves interfering (Alex Filippenko)

Wave interference pattern (Alex Filippenko)

Production of Doppler effect (Saunders College Publishing)

Isotopes of H and He (Saunders College Publishing)

Trilobite, lower Cambrian (Bill Schopf)

Stromatolites, oldest fossil (Bill Schopf)

Jupiter, Io, and Europa from 20 million km (Jet Propulsion Labs)

Star map: Leo constellation (Science Graphics)

Southern Milky Way from alpha-Cen to eta-Car (James Curry)

Moon at apogee and perigee (James Curry)

Spacetime curvature (Alex Filippenko)

Dinosaur watching comet crash (Walter Alvarez)

Io Composed from Several Frames (Jet Propulsion Labs)

HR diagram with main classes marked (Saunders College Publishing)

Star trails South Celestial Pole (Anglo-Australian Observatory, Photograph By David Malin #6, c 1980.)

CCD chip, schematic (Alex Filippenko)

Changing view of night sky (Alex Filippenko)

The Sun, schematic (Alex Filippenko)

Solar eclipses, schematic (Alex Filippenko)

Star and spectrum, schematic (Alex Filippenko)

Human skull, top half. (Alex Filippenko)

The 3.9 meter Anglo-Australian telescope (Anglo-Australian Observatory, Photograph By David Malin Board, 1977)

Hubble Space Telescope in orbit (NASA)

1979 solar eclipse, partial phase in clouds (Alex Filippenko)

1979 solar eclipse, diamond ring (Alex Filippenko)

1979 solar eclipse, totality (Alex Filippenko)

Weekly World News headline: 5 US Senators are Space Aliens!(Weekly World News)

Universe models and geometry (Saunders College Publishing)

Comet Hale-Bopp and Keck domes (Richard Wainscoat)

Scientific Notation (Alex Filippenko)

Light year: distance light travels in 1 year (Alex Filippenko)

Common Prefixes (Alex Filippenko)

Units, metric system (Alex Filippenko)

Angular measure (Alex Filippenko)

Electronic transitions that produce emission lines, hydrogen (Saunders College Publishing)

Geometry of lunar eclipse (Saunders College Publishing)

Chromatic aberration (Saunders College Publishing)

Hale 200-inch (5-m) telescope; Russell Porter drawing. (Hale Observatories, California Institute of Technology)

Solar eclipse paths on Earth (Sky and Telescope)

Stefan-Boltzmann law (Alex Filippenko)

Celestial sphere: why we see half of it (Alex Filippenko)

Lines of force for a proton (Alan Guth)

Lines of force for a bar magnet, 2 magnets (Alan Guth)

The Galactic Center (ANGLO-AUSTRALIAN OBSERVATORY, PHOTOGRAPH BY DAVID MALIN #28, C 1980.)

The Compton Effect (Alex Filippenko)

Luminosity L, from surface area and Stefan-Boltzmann law (Alex Filippenko)

Wave/particle duality of normal matter (Alex Filippenko)

Wien's law, numerically (Alex Filippenko)

Why a total lunar eclipse looks orange/red (Alex Filippenko)

Inflating bubble, with grid lines (Alan Guth)

Light Travel Time: Moon example (Alex Filippenko)

Light travel time is proportional to distance (Alex Filippenko)

H atom: ground state (Alex Filippenko)

Chalkboard full of equations (Alex Filippenko)

Keck mirror - honeycomb (California Association for Research in Astronomy)

Mauna Kea summit - snow covered (Alex Filippenko)

Alex and students at the beach in Hawaii (Alex Filippenko)

Two Keck telescopes illuminated inside (Serge Brunier)

SOFIA telescope, in airplane (NASA)

Drawing of Hubble Space Telescope looking at galaxy (NASA)

Midnight sun at South Pole (James Lloyd)

Sunset at South Pole (James Lloyd)

Bending of starlight by Sun, measured by Eddington (Alex Filippenko)

X-ray view of solar corona (NASA)

Reversal of magnetic polarity during sunspot cycle (Alex Filippenko)

Sun's rotation affects magnetic field lines (Saunders College Publishing)

Diagram showing why sunsets are red (Alex Filippenko)

Geometry of solar eclipse (Saunders College Publishing)

1979 total solar eclipse, very cloudy partial phase (Alex Filippenko)

Orange gibbous moon rising over trees (Alex Filippenko)

NGC 2997 (#17) (Anglo-Australian Observatory, Photograph By David Malin)

Halley's Comet On 12 March 1986 (#19)

Star Trails In The South West (Anglo-Australian Observatory, Photograph By David Malin #5, C 1980)

The Cluster Of Galaxies In Virgo (Anglo-Australian Observatory/Royal Observatory, Edingurgh, Photograph By David Malin)

Before And After Supernova 1987a (Anglo-Australian Observatory, Photograph By David Malin)

The Giant Elliptical Galaxy M87 (Anglo-Australian Observatory, Photograph By David Malin)

Interference pattern with plane-parallel incident light (Richard Wolfson and The Teaching Company)

2-slit pattern with particles and waves (Richard Wolfson and The Teaching Company)